THE STORY OF THE ATOM

THE STORY OF THE ATOM

by

J. A. HARRISON, M.A., M.Ed., Ph.D.

HULTON EDUCATIONAL PUBLICATIONS

© J. A. Harrison

1959

71750111 6

First published 1959 by

HULTON EDUCATIONAL PUBLICATIONS

55/59 Saffron Hill, London E. C. 1.

Printed in Great Britain by

Cox & Wyman Ltd., London, Reading and Fakenham.

Reprinted lithographically in 1965 by

Dai Nippon Printing Co. (International) Ltd., Hong Kong

Reprinted 1968

CONTENTS

ACKNOWLEDGEMENTS

Several of the illustrations in this book are taken from the film *Conquest of the Atom*, a 20-minute film produced by Mullard Ltd. in conjuction with the Educational Foundation for Visual Aids, 33 Queen Anne Street, London, W.1.

Other acknowledgements for photographs are due to: *Radio Times* Hulton Picture Library; The Science Museum; Philips Electrical Ltd.; Central Office of Information; The British Petroleum Co. Ltd.; Cavendish Laboratory; Watson & Sons (Electro-Medical) Ltd., North Wembley; Barratt's Photo Press Ltd.; Camera Press Ltd.; Atomic Energy Research Establishment, Harwell; U.K. Atomic Energy Authority; Central Press Photos, Ltd.; General Electric Co. Ltd.; Wakefields Ltd., Chiswick; Associated Electrical Industries, Ltd.

The photograph of Becquerel (opposite p. 36) is taken from *The Nobel Prize Winners and The Nobel Foundation 1901–37* by J. W. MacCallum and Dr. Stephen Taylor, published by The Central European Times Publishing Co. Ltd., Zürich.

CHAPTER 1

The Atom, The Smallest Particle

THERE have been several periods in history when a great discovery or invention produced revolutionary changes in man's way of living. Such was the discovery and use of bronze and iron. Later, in the eighteenth and nineteenth centuries, the invention and development of the steam engine harnessed the energy of coal and led inevitably to the Industrial Revolution. Today we are in the early stages of another revolutionary change —the harnessing of atomic energy. Enormous forces are now available to man either for his service or for his destruction.

This is the story of how this came about, of how the atom was explored and finally conquered. It begins in Greece more than 2,300 years ago. At that time the philosopher-scientist Democritus advanced the theory that matter was made up of very small indivisible particles. Suppose, for example, we consider a piece of soil. This can be crushed into dust, but the particles of dust can be ground into finer particles. Eventually, however, argued Democritus, a stage is reached when the particles cannot be further subdivided or cut up. It was Democritus who gave us the word "atom" for these, the smallest indivisible particles of matter; he used the Greek word "atomos" which means something that cannot be cut. He believed that the Universe consisted of atoms which were created eternally and remained for ever unchanged; he imagined them as minute hard spheres, indestructible and indivisible.

Aristotle, another Greek philosopher, was born while Democritus was still alive. He did not believe in the atom. His theory was that all substances were made of basic material on which different forms and properties could be impressed, much as a sculptor can make different statues from one block of marble. Aristotle chose as the really fundamental properties: hot, cold, moist and dry. By combining these in pairs he obtained what he called the four elements: fire, air, earth and water. Thus fire was

7

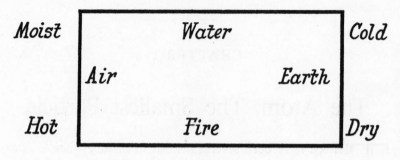

FIG. 1

hot and dry; air was hot and moist; earth was cold and dry and water was cold and moist.

It was Aristotle's theory which shaped the mind of man for nearly 2,000 years. According to his theory it should be possible to change substances from one to another and chemists, called alchemists, attempted to do so; to change, for example, base metal such as lead into gold. None of their experiments worked—except by fraud. Nevertheless the changing, or transmutation as it was called, of one substance into another remained the dream of the alchemists for many centuries. Many of these alchemists wandered over Europe in search of wealthy patrons of their worthless prescriptions for transmutation. One such fraud was to place lead in a crucible and stir with a hollow iron rod filled with gold powder and stopped with wax. When the crucible was heated the lead appeared to turn into gold. The true explanation was, of course, that the wax had melted and let the gold out of the stirring rod into the crucible to mix with the lead.

The beginning of modern Chemistry

The end of the alchemists and the beginning of modern chemistry was largely due to Robert Boyle, who was born in 1627 and died in 1691. Boyle devoted his whole life to science. He is probably best known for discovering the relation between the pressure and volume of gases called Boyle's Law. He introduced accurate experiments into chemistry and improved much of the apparatus in use in his time. These experiments led him to overthrow the doctrines of Aristotle and the alchemists. Boyle was convinced that gold could not be made. To Boyle gold was an element; he defined an element as a basic substance which could not by any known means be split into, or made from, two or more simpler substances. He believed that copper, silver, and mercury, for example, were also elements. Boyle was convinced that all the many different substances which existed in the world could be proved by experiments to consist of a relatively small number of elements. History was to prove that Boyle was right.

More than a century passed before Boyle's ideas of chemical elements were taken a stage further. It was the French scientist Lavoisier (1743–1794), famous for his experiments on combustion, who continued the work of Boyle and recognised the importance of elements in understanding the nature of matter. Lavoisier compiled the first list of elements—a total of 28. Lavoisier was executed in the French Revolution in May 1794 but scientists in many countries continued the work and used similar methods. They found that some elements could be mixed together; thus iron and copper filings could be mixed together in any proportion and the mixture had properties of both iron and copper. Other elements, however, when put together, combined to form a different chemical substance called a compound. For example, sodium, a metal which reacts violently with water, combined with chlorine, a poisonous gas, to form sodium chloride which is common salt. Sodium chlorine is a compound; its chemical properties are very different from those of sodium and chlorine. Moreover, sodium and chlorine always combine in the same proportions; when 117 ounces of salt was analysed it always contained 46 ounces of sodium and 71 ounces of chlorine. Water was found to be a compound of hydrogen and oxygen, always 1 part hydrogen and 8 parts oxygen by weight. Red mercuric oxide always had the same composition: 100 parts of mercury to 8 parts of oxygen by weight. The analysis of a larger number of compounds led, in 1799, to the French chemist Proust putting forward what is called the Law of Constant Composition. This stated that, when elements combined, they did so in definite proportions by weight so that the composition of a chemical compound was always the same.

Scientists verified the Law of Constant Composition with many experiments and published long tables of combining weights. But they could not explain why elements combined in this way. It was John Dalton who found the answer; he realised that the Law of Constant Composition could only be explained by the atom.

9

Dalton's Atomic Theory

John Dalton was born in Eaglesfield, a village near Cockermouth in Cumberland, in 1766. He came from a poor Quaker family and as a young boy earned his living partly by teaching and partly as a farm labourer. He started to teach in the village school at the age of twelve but he later moved to Manchester where he spent the rest of his life on scientific research.

In 1808 he put forward the Atomic Theory which stated that chemical elements are composed of very minute particles of matter called atoms. Atoms are the smallest particles of matter; they cannot be divided and are indestructible. All atoms of one element, said Dalton, are the same; thus all atoms of hydrogen, for example, are identical and have exactly the same weight. Different elements, however, have atoms differing in weight; those of hydrogen for example are different from those of oxygen. His theory also asserted that in chemical combination atoms of elements unite to form compound atoms called molecules, and always unite in simple numerical ratios: something like 1 : 1 or 1 : 2. For example, *one* atom of sodium combines with *one* atom of chlorine to form a molecule of sodium chloride. Every molecule of sodium chloride will therefore be the same and contain one atom of chlorine and one atom of sodium. Sodium chloride will therefore have a constant composition and the proportion of sodium to chlorine will always be the same. The Atomic Theory had explained the Law of Constant Composition.

Dalton realised that the weight of a single atom was very small indeed. He therefore directed his attention to relative weights, taking the weight of the lightest element, that of hydrogen, as unity. The weight of an atom of an element relative to the weight of an atom of hydrogen is called the Atomic Weight, and scientists who followed Dalton were able to determine the Atomic Weights of the elements. The Atomic Weight of oxygen was found to be 16, that is, an atom of oxygen is sixteen times as heavy as an atom of hydrogen. The Atomic Weight of copper is 63, of sodium 23 and so on. Gradually tables were built up giving the Atomic Weights of all known elements.

Dalton also devised symbols to represent atoms (Fig. 2). His symbol for hydrogen was ⊙ and for oxygen O. These symbols were later replaced by a much simpler system in which an atom is represented by the initial letter of the Latin name of the element —H for hydrogen, O for oxygen and so on. Thus H_2O stands for

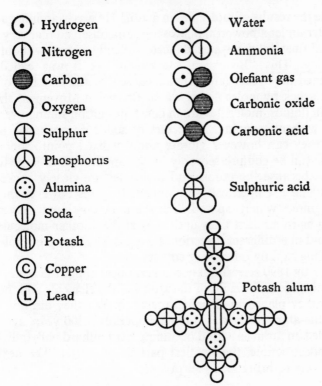

FIG. 2. Dalton's Symbols

one molecule of water, the smallest particle of water that can exist alone; it contains two atoms of hydrogen and one atom of oxygen.

Dalton's Atomic Theory therefore not only explained the Law of Constant Composition but was the starting point of even more important developments. The science of chemistry made rapid progress with the discovery of new substances and chemical reactions. Methods were discovered of measuring molecules and atoms in spite of their small size. Some idea of the size of a molecule may be obtained by imagining a drop of water magnified until it is as big as the earth; the molecules of water in the drop would only be about the size of golf balls. The atoms making up the molecule are still smaller; an atom of hydrogen weighs 1.66×10^{-24} gm. They are far too small to be seen even by the most powerful microscope. But in 1827 a botanist, Robert Brown,

11

did see the results of molecules in action. He was examining a drop of water under a powerful microscope and observed that very small bits of dust in the water danced violently about without ever stopping. This "Brownian Movement" as it was called was explained fifty years later; it was caused by the tiny bits of dust being struck by molecules of water. Brownian Movement showed that, in liquids, molecules are in constant motion sliding over each other without stopping. Molecules of solids do not move in this way; they can however vibrate about a fixed point. Solids and liquids can be compressed only by the application of large forces. This is because the atoms and molecules are closely packed together and are practically in contact. In gases however they are much more widely spaced. They are in continual movement, travelling in straight lines until they strike another molecule and rebound in a different direction. So a gas is made up of molecules travelling rapidly on zig-zag courses.

Thus by 1890 scientists knew a great deal about the atom. They knew the size and weight of the atoms of the elements and the part which they played in chemical reactions. But they did not know what the atom really was. Like Democritus 2,300 years ago, they regarded an atom as a kind of minute hard billiard ball, indivisible and indestructible, the smallest particle of matter. The next few years were to bring many surprises.

CHAPTER 2

Thomson Discovers the Electron

ABOUT 1860 scientists in a number of countries began to experiment with discharge tubes. In England Sir William Crookes was a foremost pioneer and discharge tubes are often called Crookes tubes in his honour. Early discharge tubes consisted of a long glass tube closed at both ends. A small metal plate was sealed into each end of the tube and connected to an induction coil to provide a high voltage. The plate connected to the positive terminal of the induction coil was called the anode and the other the cathode. The tube was connected to a vacuum pump so that air could be withdrawn.

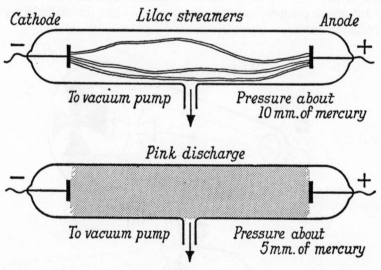

FIG. 3. Discharge tube

With the discharge tube full of air, nothing happened when the induction coil was switched on. The voltage was insufficient to enable electricity to jump the gap between cathode and anode. But

13

as air was removed from the tube by the vacuum pump, changes were seen in the tube. First lilac-coloured streamers of light passed between anode and cathode (Fig. 3). As more air was pumped out, the whole space between anode and cathode became filled with a pink glow. This colour depended on the gas in the tube; if neon was used instead of air, there was a red glow; if mercury vapour, the glow was green. If however more gas was pumped out until only a trace remained, the glow inside the tube disappeared altogether. With this high vacuum the tube was dark inside but the glass walls of the tube glowed with a green colour like the dial of a luminous watch in the dark. This green glow, called fluorescence, was soon found to be due to the presence of invisible rays coming from the direction of the cathode. They were called cathode rays; on striking the glass walls of the tube, they caused fluorescence.

The presence of these rays was demonstrated in a simple experiment by the German scientist Hittorf in 1869. He made a discharge tube which included a mica cross and showed that it cast a shadow on the end of the tube (Fig. 4). When the rays struck the tube, the glass fluoresced green, while in the shadow it remained dark. If the end of the tube is painted inside with zinc sulphide, a fluorescent paint, much greater luminosity is obtained when the cathode rays strike the surface.

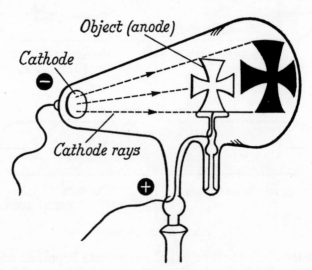

FIG. 4. Discharge tube for demonstrating that cathode rays travel in straight lines

Crookes designed a tube which contained a light mica paddle mounted on rails (Fig. 5). When the induction coil was switched on, the paddle moved along the rails from cathode to anode driven by the cathode rays.

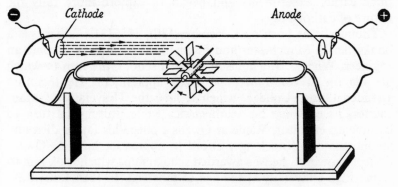

FIG. 5. Cathode rays striking the vanes of a small paddle cause it to roll from one end of tube to other

In another specially-designed discharge tube a beam of cathode rays was narrowed down to a thin pencil of rays by a slit (Fig. 6). The path of these rays was made visible by inserting in the tube a fluorescent screen consisting of a long strip of metal painted with zinc sulphide. The rays travelled straight from the cathode through the slit. When, however, the North pole of a powerful magnet was placed near the tube, the cathode rays bent downwards and a South pole bent them upwards. This showed that the rays were electrically charged and that the charge was negative, but we will deal more fully with this later.

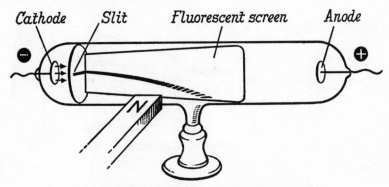

FIG. 6. Bending a beam of cathode rays by a magnet

These experiments proved to be the starting-point of a new method of studying the atom, although at the time this was not realized. The real beginning was when J. J. Thomson in the Cavendish Laboratory at Cambridge University repeated some of these earlier experiments and began to explore more fully the nature of cathode rays.

Thomson was born on December 18th, 1856. His father was a bookseller in Manchester and he intended his son to become an engineer. When J. J. Thomson finished school, the firm to which he was to go could take no more apprentices. He therefore attended Owens College, which is now the University of Manchester, to continue his mathematics while waiting his turn to become an engineer. While at Owens College his father died and his mother could no longer afford to apprentice him. At Owens College, however, he was awarded scholarships which took him to Cambridge University at the age of nineteen. In 1884 Lord Rayleigh retired as Cavendish Professor of Experimental Physics. J. J. Thomson, who was then twenty-seven, was chosen to succeed him and began what was to be a career of great distinction.

He constructed a discharge tube with a small hole at the centre of the anode (Fig. 7). Next to the anode was another plate, again with a small hole at the centre. When all but a trace of air had been removed by a vacuum pump and the induction coil switched on, a narrow beam of cathode rays passed through the two holes and produced a small bright spot on the fluorescent screen at P. Also, in the tube he fixed two plates C and D called deflecting plates. When C was made electrically positive, the cathode ray beam was bent upwards and the spot on the fluorescent screen moved to P_1.

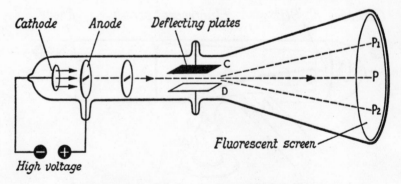

FIG. 7. Diagram of discharge tube used by J. J. Thomson

FIG. 8. Robert Boyle, 1627–1691. Boyle defined an element as a substance which cannot be split into two or more simpler substances

FIG. 9. Antoine Laurent Lavoisier, 1743–1794. Lavoisier compiled the first list of elements

FIG. 10. John Dalton, 1766–1844. Dalton introduced the first Atomic Theory

FIG. 11. Sir J. J. Thomson, 1856–1940. Thomson, in 1897, discovered the electron inside the atom

Fig. 12. Thomson at work in his laboratory

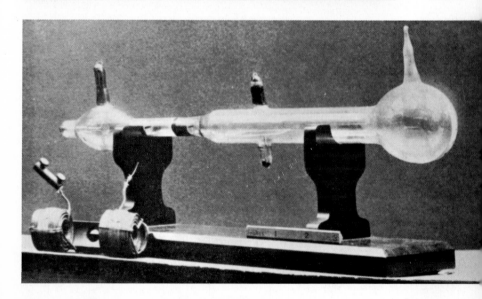

Fig. 13. Discharge tube used by Thomson in the discovery of the electron

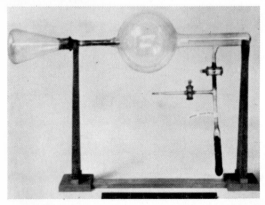

Fig. 14. Discharge tube used by Thomson in the discovery of the positive particle

Photo, Science Museum, London, reproduced by permission of the Cavendish Laboratory, Cambridge

When C was made negative the beam was bent downwards and the spot moved to P_2. As like charges repel and unlike charges attract, this showed that the cathode ray beam was negatively charged. He was able to show that the distance of the spot on the fluorescent screen depended on the voltage applied to the deflecting plates. He also carried out similar experiments in which the spot was deflected by an electro-magnet. He was able to prove that cathode rays consisted of particles, all of which were identical and negatively charged. These were called electrons. These particles were tiny; their weight was only $\frac{1}{1840}$th that of the lightest atom, hydrogen.

Thomson showed that these electrons came from the gas remaining in the tube, but whatever gas he used, the deflection was always the same. On April 30th 1897, he announced to the Royal Institution that he had found a universal constituent of matter which was much smaller than the atom. Thomson had discovered the electron within the atom.

But as well as the negatively charged cathode rays, positive rays were also discovered in the discharge tube. When a discharge tube was constructed with a hole in the cathode, a bright patch appeared on the fluorescent screen at the end of the tube (Fig. 15). This was produced by a positive ray which travelled from the anode, through the cathode to the screen. It therefore travelled in the opposite direction to the cathode ray. Thomson investigated the nature of these rays and found that they could be bent by an electric charge or a magnet. A positively-charged deflector plate, which had

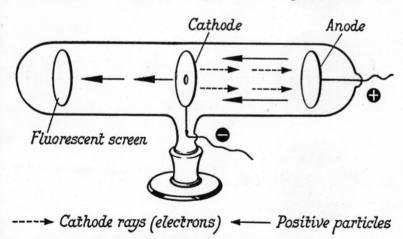

FIG. 15. Diagram showing positive rays and cathode rays

attracted the cathode ray, repelled the positive ray. He proved that positive rays consisted of positively-charged particles. He found that, unlike the electrons, the weight of these positive particles differed with the gas present in the tube. When the tube contained a trace of hydrogen, positive particles had a certain weight, but positive particles produced in a tube containing oxygen, for example, had a different weight. With hydrogen, the positive particles were almost as heavy as hydrogen atoms, with oxygen almost as heavy as oxygen atoms. This proved to be true for any gases used in the tube. So it looked as though these positive particles were the actual gas atoms minus the electrons which had been pulled out.

Thomson now visualised the atom as being a sphere with positive charges spread over it and negative electrons embedded inside. Since all atoms in their normal state are electrically neutral, the negative and positive charges must balance. Thus hydrogen, the lightest atom, would have the equivalent of one unit of positive charge and one electron to balance. The next heavier atom, helium, would have the equivalent of two units of positive charges

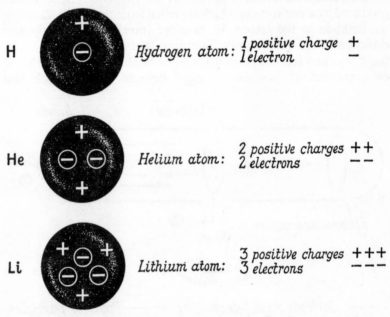

FIG. 16. Atoms are normally neutral; the number of positive and negative charges balance

and two electrons to balance. Lithium would have three and so on (Fig. 16).

With this theory, we can explain what happens in a discharge tube. Suppose the tube to begin with is filled with gas hydrogen, that is, with hydrogen atoms. Let us consider one particular atom. When the induction coil is switched on, the high positive voltage on the anode will attract the negatively-charged electron. Suppose the voltage is high enough to exert sufficient force to pull the electron out of the atom. We have now not one atom, but two separate particles with equal and opposite charges. One is the tiny negatively charged electron of weight only $\frac{1}{1840}$th that of the hydrogen atom. The other is the positive particle consisting of the remainder of the hydrogen atom; an atom with one or more electrons removed from it is called an ion, so this is usually called the hydrogen ion.

The electron will then be pulled towards the anode and the positive particle, in this case the hydrogen ion, towards the cathode But neither can move far, because they will immediately come into collision with neighbouring atoms. No current, therefore, flows and no visible change takes place in the discharge tube. If, however, a vacuum pump is used to remove hydrogen, the number of hydrogen atoms remaining in the tube is considerably reduced. These atoms will be widely spaced and a stage is reached when electrons and hydrogen ions can travel freely through the tube without danger of collision with hydrogen atoms. The tube then conducts electricity carried by the electrons and ions, and a luminous discharge appears. There is then a steady stream of electrons moving from cathode to anode forming the cathode ray and a stream of positive particles, in this case hydrogen ions, travelling from anode to cathode forming the positive ray.

In the modern world, discharge tubes are widely used. Sodium and mercury vapour lamps are used for street lighting and to mark runways at airports, neon and many other tubes for advertising signs and other types of indoor illumination. Although many technical improvements have been introduced, present-day tubes are basically the same as those discovered and used in experiments many years ago. Fluorescent tubes used for lighting are discharge tubes with the inside entirely coated with fluorescent material; the light is produced by cathode rays striking the fluorescent coating. The cathode ray tube in a television receiver, although using a different method of obtaining electrons, is clearly very similar and

21

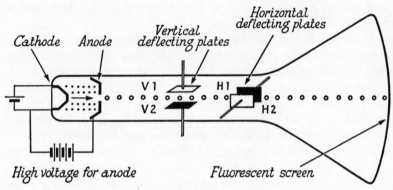

FIG. 17. Cathode ray tube

identical in principle to the cathode ray tube which Thomson designed; the method he used to deflect the cathode ray is the same as that used today to scan the picture (Fig. 17).

But this was not Thomson's major contribution to science. History was to show that the importance of his work was his discovery of the electrons and the theory of the atom. For 2,000 years, the atom had been regarded as solid and indivisible—the smallest particle of matter. Thomson proved that the atom could be separated into electrons and positive particles. Inside the atom, he found the electron which was very much smaller than the atom itself. He had opened the door to a new world, the world of atomic science.

Thomson's personality and achievements attracted to the Cavendish Laboratory a brilliant team of research scientists who were to continue his work and carry it much further. In 1906, he was awarded the Nobel Prize. This is the highest international recognition for scientific achievement and he lived to see seven of his students receive Nobel Prizes. He was knighted Sir J. J. Thomson in 1908, but to many he remained "J. J.", as he was affectionately called. He died in 1940 and was buried in Westminster Abbey, near the tombs of Newton, Darwin, Kelvin and Rutherford.

CHAPTER 3

X-Rays and Radioactivity

ONE of the interesting events in the history of science is the accidental discovery of X-rays by Röntgen in 1895, two years before Thomson announced the discovery of the electron. Röntgen, Professor þf Physics at Würzburg in Germany, while photographing a discharge tube in one of his experiments, discovered that photographic plates wrapped in black paper and left near the apparatus became fogged. Although they had been carefully wrapped in light proof paper they looked when developed as though they had been exposed to light. Röntgen found that this was due to some kind of invisible yet penetrating rays given out by the discharge tube. He did not know what they were, so he called them X-rays, the letter X meaning, as in algebra, an unknown. Sir William Crookes in some of his experiments had also been troubled with fogging of his plates, but he moved them to another room and thus possibly missed discovering X-rays.

Röntgen soon found that X-rays had some very important properties. They penetrated light metals but not heavy ones, and flesh more easily than bone. So great was their importance that within a few weeks of Röntgen's discovery, X-rays were being used in surgical operations in Vienna. For the first time doctors were able to see the bones inside the body.

Röntgen found that these unknown rays were coming from the glass walls of the discharge tubes. They came particularly from the region where the most intense beam of cathode rays struck the glass. It was discovered that they were produced whenever electrons were suddenly stopped either by striking the glass walls of the tube or by other means.

A greatly improved X-ray tube was therefore designed in which the cathode was curved like a concave mirror (Fig. 18). This focused a powerful beam of electrons on to the anode, called the target. Here the electrons were stopped and X-rays radiated in all directions, having no difficulty in passing through the glass walls of the tube.

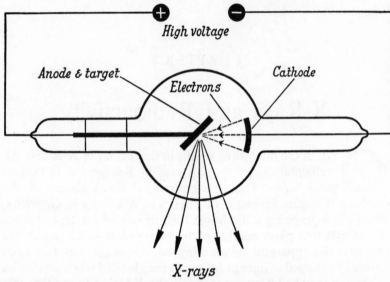

X-rays

FIG. 18. Diagram from early form of X-ray tube

Although the equipment for producing X-rays rapidly improved, the nature of the rays remained a problem for many years. It was finally proved, mainly by W. H. Bragg and his son W. L. Bragg, that X-rays were waves. They are produced when a stream of electrons strikes a target in somewhat the same way as a stream

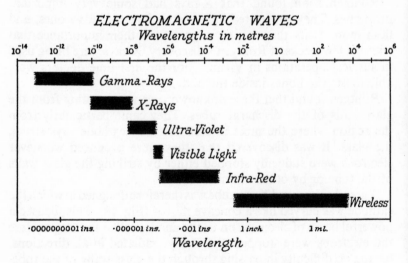

FIG. 19

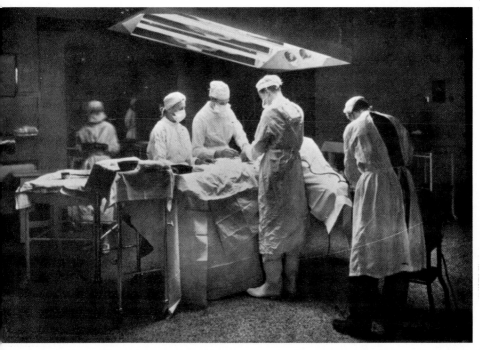

FIG. 20. Fluorescent lighting in a hospital operating theatre

FIG. 21. Sodium discharge tubes used for street lighting

FIG. 22. Röntgen, who in 1895 discovered X-rays

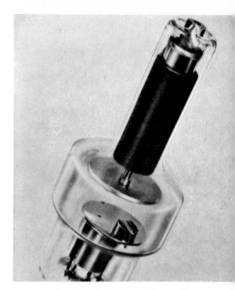

FIG. 23. A modern X-ray tube

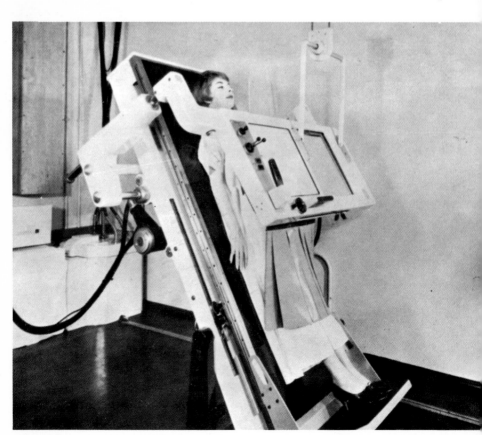

FIG. 24. Modern X-ray equipment in operation

of machine-gun bullets fired into a pond produced waves, spreading outwards from the point where the bullets strike the water's surface. X-rays were found to have similar properties to electromagnetic waves, such as light and radio waves. They travelled in straight lines and were not deflected by magnetic or electric fields; they travelled at a speed of 186,000 miles a second; they could be beamed and travel through a vacuum. X-rays differed from other electro-magnetic waves only in their wave-length; they were of much shorter wave-lengths even than light (Fig. 19).

Modern X-ray tubes are somewhat similar to the early equipment, except that a different source of electrons is used (Fig. 25). In a modern X-ray tube a tungsten wire filament at the centre of the cathode is heated by a low voltage. This provides a copious supply of electrons which on striking the target, produces a far more intense source of X-rays. A similar method of producing electrons is now employed in a television cathode ray tube or a

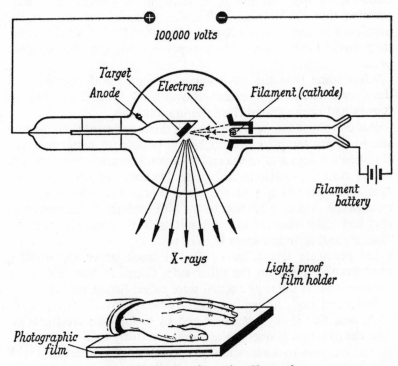

FIG. 25. Diagram of a modern X-ray tube

27

radio valve. Today, X-rays are widely used in medicine, dentistry, for seeing that shoes fit, industrially for detecting the presence of flaws and cracks in metals, and even for the analysis of complex chemical substances.

Becquerel discovers radioactivity

Röntgen's discovery in 1895 was therefore extremely important. A year later, another discovery was made which proved to be equally important. This was the discovery of radioactivity by the French scientist Becquerel. Becquerel was at that time investigating the behaviour of fluorescent substances.

Among the fluorescent substances which Becquerel tried were salts of uranium. He knew that when these substances were placed in sunlight, they glowed brilliantly. Having heard of Röntgen's X-rays, he thought that, in addition to emitting light, fluorescent substances might also emit X-rays. He therefore wrapped a photographic plate in black paper, placed some uranium on top and put it in sunlight. It glowed brilliantly, showing that the uranium salt emitted fluorescent light. If the uranium salt also gave out X-rays, these could be detected because they would penetrate the black paper and fog the photographic plate.

After some time the plate was taken into the dark-room and developed. The plate was marked with black spots just as though X-rays had been emitted from the uranium salt.

But one day when he was repeating the experiment there was no sun so he put the plate in a cupboard, hoping for better weather. It rained for days and in the end Becquerel became impatient and out of curiosity developed the plate. He could hardly believe his eyes when he found that the plate was again blackened. The penetrating rays had nothing to do with sunlight or fluorescence; they had come from the uranium salt itself. He concluded that the uranium salt gave out some kind of rays, rays which, like X-rays, could penetrate several thicknesses of black paper and affect a photographic plate on the other side. Uranium was said to be radioactive and the rays emitted were called Becquerel rays.

Becquerel rays, as well as being detected by a photographic plate can, like X-rays, be measured by a gold-leaf electroscope. The electroscope is one of the oldest electrical measuring instruments. It is easy to see how it works from a simple experiment with pith balls. Suppose we have two pith balls hanging by fine threads.

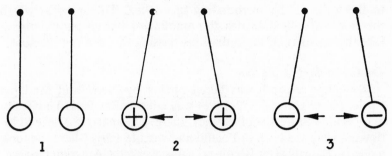

FIG. 26. Pith balls with no charge hang vertically (1) Pith balls with similar charges repel each other (2) and (3)

If the pith balls are uncharged they hang vertically. If, however, both pith balls are given the same charge they will repel each other and be pushed apart (Fig. 26). In an electroscope a thin strip of gold leaf is fastened along its upper edge to a rod of metal. The gold leaf, hanging vertically, and rod are mounted in a metal box with a glass window (Fig. 27). The rod is insulated from the box by a good insulator such as sulphur, and provided at the end with a disc. If the disc is touched momentarily with an electrically-charged body, some of the charge goes into, and distributes itself over, the rod and gold leaf. Since like charges repel each other, the gold leaf is pushed out. It will remain in this position for a considerable time. If, however, radioactive material or an X-ray tube is placed in front of the window, the gold leaf slowly falls into its normal vertical position. This is because the rays ionise the air in the box. The air therefore becomes slightly conducting and the charge on the gold leaf gradually leaks away

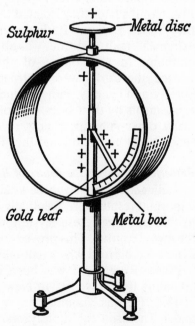

FIG. 27. Gold-leaf electroscope

29

to the walls of the surrounding metal box. The speed at which the gold leaf falls indicates the amount of ionisation and therefore the intensity of the radiations passing through the window.

The Curies discover Radium

Röntgen's research was taken further by Pierre and Madame Curie. Pierre Curie (1859–1906) was educated at Paris University and became Professor cf Physics. In 1895 he married Marie Sklodowska who was born in Poland and went to Paris where she took a degree. Shortly after Becquerel's discovery, the Austrian Government provided the Curies with a ton of uranium ore called pitchblende which was found in Bohemia. Working in the School of Physics in Paris, they used an electroscope to measure the radiation and found to their surprise that the uranium ore gave out more radiation than its uranium content could account for. They concluded that the ore must contain minute amounts of other substances which were intensely radioactive, and began the laborious task of trying to separate these substances. They isolated a new radioactive substance which was more active than uranium. They called it polonium, after Poland, Madame Curie's native country. Five months later they isolated a far more active substance, which they called radium. Radium which was present in the ore in extremely small quantities was about two million times as active as uranium. In recognition of this outstanding contribution to science, the Curies were awarded the Davy Medal of the Royal Society and (jointly with Becquerel) the Nobel Prize. Continued experiments by the Curies, and others, soon led to the isolation of many other substances now recognised as radioactive elements such as ionium, radon and thorium.

Rutherford discovers the nature of Becquerel rays

Radioactivity began to be studied in many countries and many important results were eventually discovered. First it was necessary to find out what these mysterious Becquerel rays were and why they were emitted. This proved to be a difficult problem and it was Ernest Rutherford who eventually found the answer.

Ernest Rutherford was born in New Zealand in 1871. After attending the University in New Zealand, he came to Cambridge in 1895. He was Thomson's first overseas student. After working under Thomson for three years, he was appointed Professor of Physics first at the McGill University, Montreal, Canada, and then, in 1907, at Manchester University. In 1919 Thomson became Master of Trinity College, Cambridge, and Rutherford succeeded him as Professor at the Cavendish Laboratory.

It was Rutherford, with his experimental genius, who succeeded in unravelling the mystery surrounding the nature of Becquerel rays. He showed that Becquerel rays consisted not of one, but of two, different kinds of rays and shortly afterwards a third type was discovered by Villard. Radium was extremely precious and only available in very small quantities, but Madame Curie's laboratory provided the amounts needed for his experiments. His first experiment in a simplified form is illustrated in Fig 28. A small sample of radium was dropped to the bottom of a hole drilled in a block of lead. The Becquerel rays left the hole in a narrow beam. When electrically-charged plates, like the deflecting plates in Thomson's cathode ray tube, were placed at the sides of the beam, some of the rays were deflected to the left, some to the right and some not at all. A similar result was obtained if a magnet was used instead of deflector plates. The rays which were deflected towards the negative deflecting plate he called alpha rays; those deflected towards the positive plate he called beta rays and those which were not deflected at all were Villard's gamma rays.

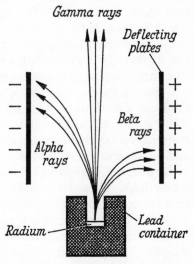

FIG. 28. Bending of Becquerel rays in an electric field

The gamma rays were electromagnetic rays; they were very similar to X-rays, except that they were of much shorter wave-length. Gamma rays were even more penetrating than X-rays; they could pass through an inch or more of lead.

As the beta rays were attracted to the positive deflecting plate, they were clearly negatively-charged (unlike charges attract). It was soon to be discovered that, like cathode rays in the discharge tube, the beta rays consisted of electrons. The electrons left

31

the radium at enormous speeds, almost equalling the speed of light, and could penetrate thin sheets of metal.

The alpha rays, on the other hand, were attracted to the negative deflecting plate, showing that they were positively charged. They were positively-charged particles; they were emitted by the radium at great speeds varying between $\frac{1}{100}$ and $\frac{1}{10}$ the velocity of light, that is, between 1,860 and 18,600 miles per second. They could travel 3 to 4 inches in air before collision with the atom of the gases of the air finally brought them to rest. They had much less penetrating power than gamma or beta rays, but could pass through very thin sheets of metal such as aluminium or gold.

Another property of alpha rays is that they produce fluorescence. Crookes devised a piece of apparatus, which he called a spinthariscope, to show this. This consisted of a hollow brass tube in which he mounted a tiny piece of radioactive material and behind this a fluorescent screen painted with zinc sulphide. At the other end of the tube he mounted a lens. On looking through the lens an enlarged image of the screen is seen and it has the appearance of a shower of sparks. The reason for this is that each alpha particle produces a flash when it hits the fluorescent screen. You can see this for yourself with a luminous dial of a watch. The luminous material on the dial consists of a mixture of radioactive material and fluorescent paint. As the alpha particles fly out of the radioactive material, they strike the fluorescent paint, each one producing a tiny flash. These tiny flashes—there are a large number every second—make the dial glow in the dark, but under a microscope the dial looks like a firework display.

Thomson had proved that the positive particles which produced the positive ray in a discharge tube consisted of atoms minus one or more electrons called ions. Rutherford set out to discover whether the positive particles emitted from radium were also ions and if so, of what atom. Using methods similar to those of Thomson, he measured the deflection of alpha particles and calculated that the alpha particles were approximately four times as heavy as hydrogen atoms. This suggested that alpha particles were ions of helium—atoms of the element helium minus electrons. Later Rutherford carried out an experiment which conclusively demonstrated the composition of alpha particles, but to understand this experiment it is necessary to know something about an apparatus called a spectroscope.

Sir Isaac Newton showed that, when a narrow beam of sunlight passed through a glass prism, it became a coloured band called a spectrum. The spectroscope is simply a piece of apparatus which produces a narrow beam of light which passes through a glass prism and a telescope for viewing the spectrum. If the spectroscope is pointed towards bright daylight or light from, say, a car head-lamp bulb, a continuous band of colour light is seen in which all the colours of the rainbow mingle one into the next. A bunsen burner produces little light; if this is placed in front of the spectroscope, nothing is seen in the telescope. But if a small amount of common salt, sodium chloride, is burned in the bunsen flame, a bright yellow line is seen in the telescope. Potassium chloride would produce a violet line. The same effect is obtained if a discharge tube is used instead of the bunsen burner. If the discharge tube contains a trace of neon, a red line would be seen. Each element has characteristic spectrum lines which, like finger-prints, can be used for identification. The spectroscope is, moreover, an extremely sensitive method of detection. Bunsen, who was one of the first scientists to experiment with this method, showed that the spectroscope could detect $\frac{1}{14,000,000,000}$ of a gram of sodium in the bunsen flame.

Rutherford used the spectroscope in his experiments. He devised a piece of apparatus which he called an alpha-trap; in this he collected alpha particles in a small discharge tube. After several days he connected the tube to an induction coil and examined the luminous discharge in a spectroscope. In the telescope he saw the characteristic yellow lines of helium. He had conclusively proved that alpha particles were helium ions.

The nature of the rays emitted by radioactive substance was now clear. They were of three kinds: alpha rays consisting of positive helium ions, beta rays consisting of negative electrons and gamma rays which were electro-magnetic waves similar to X-rays but of shorter wave-length (Fig. 29).

Theory of radioactivity

But what was the explanation of radioactivity; why were rays emitted? Rutherford and his colleague Soddy found the answer in 1903. Their theory was that atoms of radioactive elements explode with great violence, hurling out alpha and beta particles and being changed in the process to a different element. A radium atom weighs 226 times more than a hydrogen atom; its Atomic Weight is 226. The Atomic Weight of an alpha particle is 4. So, when a

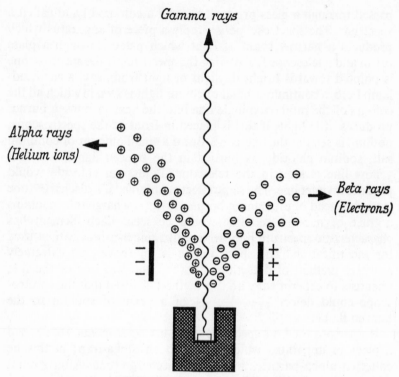

FIG. 29. Rays emitted by radioactive substances

radium atom shoots out an alpha particle, it loses 4 units of weight and becomes a new element with an Atomic Weight of 222. The name of this element is radon, but it too is radioactive; it explodes and transforms into still another element. Finally, by a process of successive break-downs, the original radium atom is transformed into an atom of the metal lead. After that, no further change takes place as lead is a stable non-radioactive element.

The Curies had shown that the supply of energy from radium was prodigious and apparently inexhaustible; it provided enough heat every hour to raise its own weight of water from freezing to boiling-point. If a piece of radium was put in a thimble of water, the water would get hot. If the thimble were insulated to prevent heat loss, then the water would boil, and continue to boil for years.

According to Rutherford and Soddy, this energy was released

when atoms exploded. But the source of this energy was a mystery until 1905 when the famous German scientist, Einstein, in working out the theory of relativity, arrived at a number of simple equations. One of these was $E = m \times c^2$ which proved to be one of the most important equations in science. E stands for energy, m for mass or matter, and c for the velocity of light. The equation means that mass can be turned into energy and energy into mass. In other words, mass is a form of energy, for if a quantity of mass could be annihilated, a definite amount of energy would be produced. As c, the speed of light, is 186,000 miles per second, c^2 is 34,596,000,000. This enormous number multiplied by the mass equals the amount of energy produced if the mass is annihilated. The amount of energy which would be produced if 1 gm. of matter could be annihilated would be about the same as that produced by burning 4,000 tons of coal. What happened when the atoms of radium exploded was that a certain amount of mass disappeared, thus producing a large amount of energy mainly in the form of heat.

Here, then, in radioactive substances was a miraculous storehouse of energy, a fuel many thousands of times more concentrated than coal. If only it could be made to "burn" more quickly. All kinds of chemical actions were tried; heat and pressure were applied; nothing had the slightest effect. Radium, uranium, polonium and all other radioactive substances continued to produce energy, each at its own speed. Nothing could be done to speed up the process, and thus liberate energy more quickly.

It was found that for radium one part in about 500,000 will break up every day, so that after 1,600 years only half the original amount remains and the radiation will be only half as strong. This span of time is called the "half-life" of radium; thus 1 gm. of radium is reduced to $\frac{1}{2}$ gm. in 1,600 years, to $\frac{1}{4}$ gm. in a further 1,600 years and so on. Thus, although it gives out a lot of energy, the rate at which it does so is very, very slow. There is no way of controlling, accelerating or stopping this process.

The half-life of radioactive elements differs. For uranium it is over 4,000 million years, for polonium 140 days (Fig. 30), while for others it is only minutes or seconds. An element with a short half-life is changing rapidly and is therefore a much stronger radiator than an element with a long half-life; the short-lived radium is more than 2 million times more radioactive than the long-lived uranium.

Rutherfors's explanation of radioactivity was a shock to

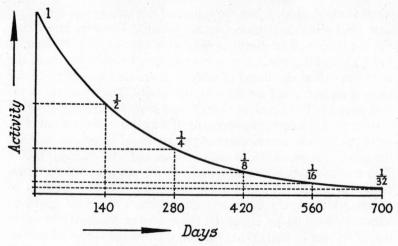

F<small>IG</small>. 30. Rate of polonium decay: half-life 140 days

scientists at the time and aroused much opposition. It destroyed the atom of Dalton and the element of Boyle. Radioactive elements, unlike the elements of Boyle, were not permanent; they changed of their own accord into different elements; an atom of the element uranium, for example, changed into radium and later into lead. Nor could an atom of an element be regarded as indestructible. Thomson had shown that atoms could be separated into electrons and positive particles. Rutherford had proved that alpha and beta particles were ejected from the interior of radioactive atoms. The atom could no longer be regarded as indivisible, the smallest particle of matter. But what was the internal structure of the atom? This was the next problem: to find the answer Rutherford decided to try and explore inside the atom.

FIG. 31. Becquerel, who in 1896 discovered
radioactivity

FIG. 32. Madame Curie (1867–1936), who
discovered radium in 1898

FIG. 33. Einstein, who in 1905 showed the
equivalence of mass and energy

FIG. 34. Lord Rutherford (1871–1937) who
discovered the nature of radioactivity and
the electrical structure of the atom

FIG. 35. Rutherford's room in the Cavendish Laboratory, Cambridge

FIG. 36. Rutherford (*right*) in the Cavendish Laboratory

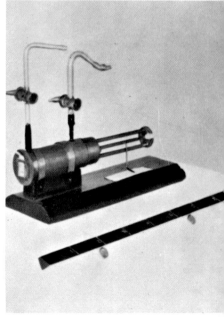

FIG. 37. Apparatus used by Rutherford to split the atom for the first time, turning nitrogen into oxygen

CHAPTER 4

Rutherford Splits the Atom

THE method which Rutherford devised to explore inside the atom was to shoot at it with alpha particles. At one side of his apparatus he enclosed a piece of radium in a lead block. The lead block had a hole in it which allowed alpha particles to escape in one direction only. The alpha particles, travelling at a speed of about 10,000 miles per second, shot out through the hole in a narrow stream like bullets from a machine gun. In their path he placed a piece of gold foil. At the other end of the apparatus there was a fluorescent screen with a microscope attached. Alpha particles which passed through the gold foil would strike the screen and flashes could be seen through the microscope just as in a spinthariscope. In this way he could see what happened when alpha particles hit atoms of gold. The apparatus was connected to a pump and evacuated so that there were no air molecules to impede the alpha particles.

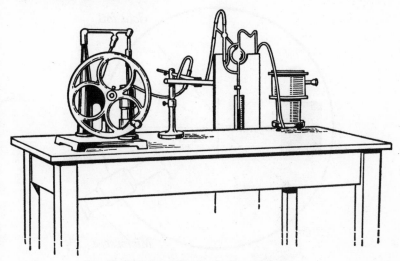

FIG. 38. Diagram of Rutherford's experiment

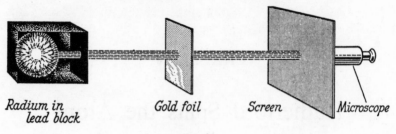

Radium in lead block   Gold foil   Screen   Microscope

FIG. 39

The screen and microscope were arranged so that they could be turned in any direction. First he placed the microscope so that it pointed directly into the hole in the lead block. The fluorescent screen was in the direct line of fire of the atomic machine-gun and plenty of flashes could be seen in the microscope as the alpha particles bullets struck the screen. He then put the thin piece of gold foil, less than one hundred thousandth of an inch thick, in the path of the alpha particles between the gun and the screen. Flashes could still be seen—proof that alpha particles had passed straight through the gold foil.

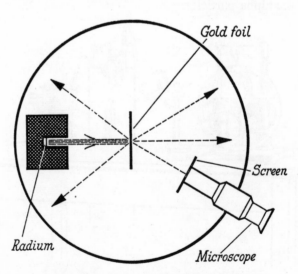

FIG. 40. Diagram of Rutherford's apparatus

Keeping the gun and gold foil in the same position, Rutherford now turned the microscope to one side away from the line of fire (Fig. 40). Flashes could still be seen. In fact, wherever the microscope was placed, there were still a few flashes—showing that when the alpha particles struck the gold foil they were scattered in all directions. The experiment showed that most alpha particles pass straight through the gold foil; a few, however, passed through but were deflected from their straight course and a few were thrown back without passing through. Some even bounced off the gold foil back along the path they had come. "It was almost as incredible as if you had fired a fifteen inch shell at a sheet of tissue paper and it came back and hit you," said Rutherford.

Now gold is a solid so its atoms are tightly packed together. If these atoms were solid like billiard balls all the alpha particles would have bounced off them and none would have gone through. Rutherford's experiment showed that practically all the alpha particles went straight through the gold. He concluded therefore that gold atoms must consist largely of empty space; all the weight of the atom must be concentrated in a small area which he called the nucleus.

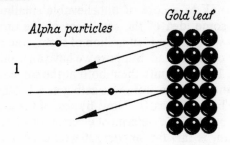

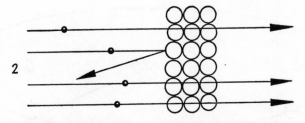

FIG. 41. If the gold atoms had been solid spheres, all the alpha particles would have bounced back (1). Most of the alpha particles have gone straight through (2)

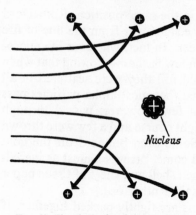

FIG. 42. The closer the alpha particles get to the nucleus, the more sharply they are deflected

This nucleus must carry the positive charge. As the alpha particles were also positively charged, the nucleus would repel any alpha particles coming within its field (Fig. 42). As only 1 in 8,000 alpha particles bounced back or was deflected, the nucleus of the atom had to be very, very small. Rutherford therefore saw the atom as a central positively charged nucleus with one or more electrons circling round it like planets round the sun (Fig. 43).

From the number of alpha particles deflected, he was able to estimate that the diameter of the nucleus of an atom must be of the order of 10^{-13} cms. compared with 10^{-8} cms. for the diameter of the atom itself. The atom therefore consisted almost entirely of empty space; the substance of the atom had shrunk to a core of unbelievable smallness.

Let us try to get some idea of the smallness of the atom and nucleus. The atom is so small that ten million of them, side by side, would scarcely show on a pinhead. Suppose we have an atom and a football side by side. If we magnify them both at the same rate, we would find that, by the time the atom was as big as a football, the football would be as big as the earth. Now, by size of the atom, we mean the size of the orbit of the outermost electron or planet. The nucleus itself, the sun, is far, far smaller; it would be about the size of a speck of dust, too small to see, and the rest of the atom would be completely empty.

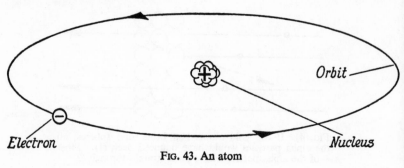

FIG. 43. An atom

At first sight it is difficult to understand how hard matter, such as your house or table, can be made up of particles which consist of so much empty space. The reason for this is the enormous speed at which the electrons travel round their orbits. When an aeroplane propeller is rotating at speed, its path appears and acts as though it were solid. Now the speed of the tip of an aeroplane propeller is much less than the speed of electrons in their orbits round the nucleous, and this is why the atom appears so solid.

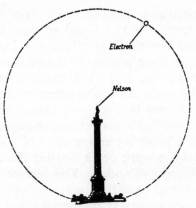

FIG. 44. If a nut on the top of Nelson's column represents the nucleus, the nearest electron will be the length of the column away

It is, however, possible, by using suitable timing gear, to shoot machine-gun bullets through the gap between the blades of a propeller which is rotating. This is because the bullets are travelling at such high speeds. In exactly the same way alpha particles and other atomic bullets move so fast that they can pass through the circling electrons, which seem to us such a solid barrier.

The nucleus was different for different elements; the nucleus of the lightest atom in the table of elements, hydrogen, had a single positive charge. Rutherford called this a proton. As the atom in its normal state is electrically neutral it would have one

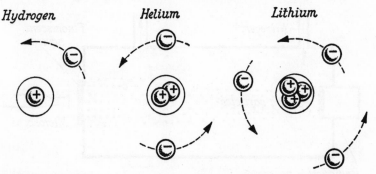

Hydrogen	Helium	Lithium
Protons in nucleus: 1	Protons in nucleus: 2	Protons in nucleus: 3
Electrons in orbit: 1	Electrons in orbit: 2	Electrons in orbit: 3

FIG. 45. Atoms of hydrogen, helium and lithium

43

electron to balance. The heavier helium nucleus had two positive charges—it was found to have two protons. The helium atom had two electrons to balance. Lithium, the third element, would have three protons in the nucleus and three electrons to balance and so on. In 1911 Rutherford had discovered the nucleus inside the atom and the structure of the atom itself.

A year later a young Danish mathematician called Niels Bohr joined Rutherford's research team. He found Rutherford's concept of a planetary arrangement of the atom not only sound, but was able to work out a detailed theory of his own which supported Rutherford's ideas. This picture of the atom is therefore often referred to as the Rutherford-Bohr atom. Although in later years much more was discovered about the atom, Rutherford's concept of a central positive nucleus with electrons circling round it still remains valid today.

Rutherford splits the atom with alpha particles

We have seen that it is fairly easy to detach electrons from atoms; Thomson had done this in his discharge tube experiments. But what about the nucleus itself? Was it divisible? Could the tiny nuclei in the centre of the atoms be hit and split with alpha particles? If so, would the resulting fragments form atoms of other elements? These were Rutherford's next problems.

This is how he set about it. The apparatus which he used is still preserved in the Cavendish Laboratory. It is so small that it could almost be slipped into a coat pocket. It consists of a cylinder

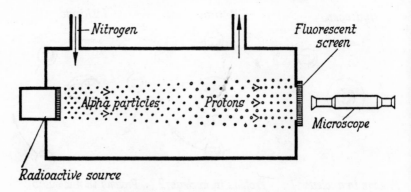

FIG. 46. Diagram of apparatus used by Rutherford to split the nitrogen atom

containing nitrogen which was placed in a powerful magnetic field. At one end of the cylinder there was a plate holding a small piece of radium. The radium, as we have seen, emits alpha particles. Rutherford hoped that some of these would hit the target—the nuclei of nitrogen. At the other end of the cylinder there was a fluorescent screen and microscope. Flashes could be seen on the screen. Now the alpha particles could only travel about half the length of the cylinder so these could not have produced the flashes. Rutherford was able to show that the flashes were produced not by alpha particles but by protons. Since there was nothing but nitrogen in the cylinder the protons must have come from the nitrogen atoms.

Later the explanation became clear. This is what had happened: Nitrogen is number seven on the table of elements; there are seven protons in the nucleus. An alpha particle (2 protons) hits a nitrogen nucleus (7 protons), making 9 protons in all. One proton was ejected and, hitting the screen, caused a flash. Eight protons were left. The nucleus with 8 protons is that of oxygen. Rutherford

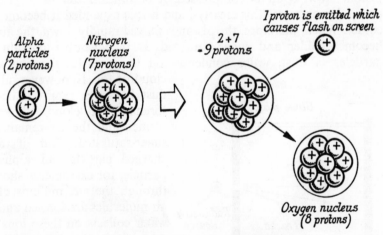

FIG. 47. Transmutation of nitrogen into oxygen

had succeeded in splitting the nucleus; he had turned nitrogen into oxygen. It was the first time a nucleus had been split.

The properties of an atom depend on the number of protons in the nucleus. Splitting the nucleus and changing the number of protons therefore changes the atom into a different element. Splitting the nucleus is therefore generally called splitting the atom. Rutherford carried out this experiment in 1919: it was the first artificial transmutation of an element.

Wilson's Cloud Chamber

A few years later, in 1925, the young scientist Blackett provided visual proof that the nitrogen atom had been split in Rutherford's experiment. He used a piece of apparatus called a cloud chamber, which had been invented by C. T. R. Wilson in 1912.

Water, if left in contact with a limited volume of air, will evaporate until the air is saturated with water vapour. The amount of water needed to saturate the air is greater at high temperatures. If saturated air is suddenly cooled, it will hold more water than it normally contains at this temperature. It is then super-saturated. The excess moisture will condense on anything at hand, a speck of dust or a charged atom for example. This is the principle on which the cloud chamber is based.

Saturated water-vapour is contained in a chamber fitted with a piston. Now, if air is compressed, it becomes hotter (a bicycle pump demonstrates this clearly), and if it is expanded it becomes colder. When, therefore, the piston is moved rapidly down, the air becomes colder and super-saturated. If the chamber contains particles of dust, water condenses on the particles forming a cloud or fog. If, however, all dust has been removed beforehand, no cloud will be formed and the air remains super-saturated. But if a charged particle, an alpha particle, for example, is shot through the air, millions of air molecules are ionised and water collects on these ions. As a result, the path of the particle is marked by a cloud track—in much the same way as the path of an aeroplane is left visible by its vapour trail.

Fig. 49 shows the kind of result obtained with a cloud

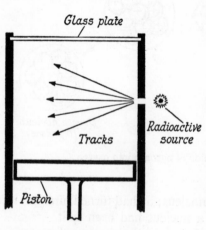

FIG. 48 Diagram of Wilson's cloud chamber

FIG. 49. *Right:* Cloud chamber: alpha particle tracks in nitrogen showing splitting of nitrogen atom

FIG. 50. Tracks of alpha particles from thorium

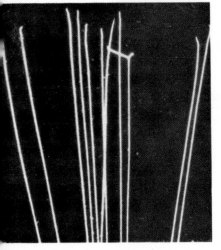

FIG. 51. Wilson's cloud chamber apparatus

FIG. 52. Cockcroft-Walton apparatus in Cavendish Laboratory—the apparatus used to split the atom with protons in 1932

FIG. 53. THE MEN WHO SPLIT THE ATOM
Left to right: Dr. E. S. Walton, Lord Rutherford and Dr. J. D. Cockcroft, who split the atom at Cavendish Laboratory, Cambridge, in 1932

FIG. 54. Dr. J. D. Cockcroft with the apparatus he used in the Cavendish Laboratory in 1932

chamber. Here the tracks of alpha particles emitted from a radioactive substance have been photographed. A great deal of research has been carried out with cloud chambers, including measurements of the speed of different particles. Rutherford described the cloud chamber as "the most original and wonderful instrument in scientific history", and it is still of great value in atomic research.

In Blackett's experiment the chamber contained nitrogen. In Fig. 49 we can see what happened. The almost parallel tracks are those of the alpha particles. We see that one alpha particle has entered a nitrogen atom, ejected a proton (the long track going off to the left) and become oxygen (the short track veering to the right). This provided visual proof that the atom had been split.

Rutherford had certainly made momentous discoveries. He had discovered the nucleus inside the atom and had measured its unbelievably small size. He had succeeded in splitting it and discovered that the fragments formed atoms of other elements. This was the first artificial transmutation of an element—the old dream of the alchemists had come true. Of course, the amount of nitrogen turned into oxygen was very minute but Rutherford showed that the same methods could be applied to other elements. After 1919 he and his collaborator Chadwick showed that almost a dozen elements could be transmuted. They turned fluorine into neon, sodium into magnesium, aluminium into silicon and phosphorus into sulphur. All these atoms were split with alpha-particles emitted from radium.

Cockcroft and Walton split the atom with protons

If alpha-particles could be used as bullets to split atoms, could not protons also be used? Two of Rutherford's colleagues, Dr. Cockcroft and Dr. Walton, set out to discover whether this was possible. First they needed a source of protons. They used one of J. J. Thomson's discharge tubes containing a trace of hydrogen. We have seen that, when a voltage was applied to the electrodes, the electrons were pulled out of the atoms, leaving behind the nuclei (Thomson's positive particles). The nucleus of a hydrogen atom is a proton, so a plentiful supply of bullets could easily be produced. The alpha-particles which Rutherford used shot out of the radioactive elements at a speed of about 10,000 miles per second and were therefore effective bullets. The next problem which Cockcroft and Walton faced was to develop equipment to speed up the protons to very high velocities, high enough to penetrate an atom. This was done with an accelerator tube, using high voltages of about 300,000 to attract the protons. The high speed protons thus produced were shot at the target which consisted of a lithium plate, and the result observed with a fluorescent screen and microscope. In Fig. 54 we see Dr. Cockcroft, now Sir John Cockcroft, examining the apparatus which he built in 1932. This is how he described the experiment:

"A transformer was used to step up the electricity from the mains to a high voltage which was then further multiplied several times and rectified in this glass tower to make it flow in one direction only. Finally, the electricity was stored in condensers. A positive voltage of about 300,000 was reached.

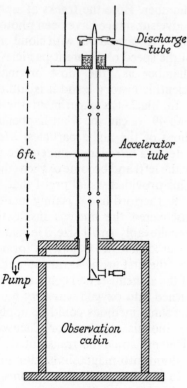

FIG. 55. Diagram of Cockcroft-Walton apparatus

This voltage was applied to the accelerator tube. At the top was one of J. J. Thomson's discharge tubes in which hydrogen atoms were pulled apart into electrons and protons. The protons travelled through a hole into the highly-evacuated glass cylinders underneath where the positive voltage accelerated them to energies of 300,000 volts. The accelerated protons struck a lithium plate at the rate of a million million per second. The lithium nuclei were the targets, but most of the protons passed between them. Only *one* proton in a thousand million scored a direct hit on a lithium nucleus, splitting it in two. The fragments flew off, some of them striking a zinc sulphide screen at the side, thus causing flashes. We observed the screen through the microscope and we could clearly see flashes, each a visual proof that a lithium nucleus had been split."

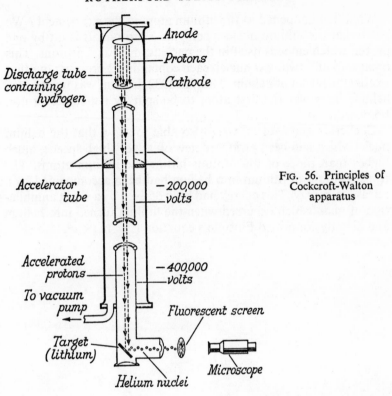

Anode

Protons

Discharge tube containing hydrogen

Cathode

Accelerator tube

−200,000 volts

FIG. 56. Principles of Cockcroft-Walton apparatus

Accelerated protons

−400,000 volts

To vacuum pump

Fluorescent screen

Target (lithium)

Microscope

Helium nuclei

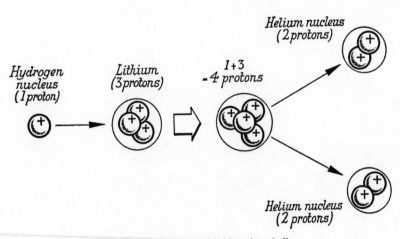

Hydrogen nucleus (1 proton)

Lithium (3 protons)

1+3 = 4 protons

Helium nucleus (2 protons)

Helium nucleus (2 protons)

FIG. 57 Transmutation of lithium into helium

51

What had happened to the lithium atom in the experiment? We know that the lithium nucleus contains 3 protons. It is hit by one proton which embeds itself in the nucleus, making 4 protons. This breaks up into two new nuclei, each containing 2 protons: in other words, the nuclei of helium. Thus, in 1932, lithium was turned into helium. This was the first atom to be split by deliberate proton bombardment.

Cockcroft and Walton were also able to show that the helium nuclei which had been produced flew off at very high speeds, much higher than those of the protons hitting the lithium atoms. The transmutation of lithium into helium had been accompanied by a release of energy. This energy had been derived by a slight annihilation of mass which occurred when the lithium turned into helium and directly confirmed Einstein's equation $E = m \times c^2$.

CHAPTER 5

The Discovery of the Neutron and the Structure of the Atom

IN 1932 Rutherford's collaborator Chadwick, now Sir James Chadwick, was experimenting on the bombardment of the metal beryllium with alpha-particles. He used a detector which could detect charged particles. The detector placed at A showed that charged particles were present; these were the alpha-particles emitted by the radioactive material. At B there were no charged particles. So the alpha-particles were being absorbed by the beryllium. At C there were charged particles; these were protons and were shooting out of the paraffin wax.

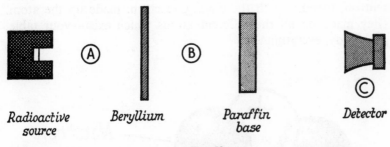

| Radioactive source | Beryllium | Paraffin base | Detector |

Fig. 58

Thus alpha-particles were going in at one end and protons coming out at the other, with apparently nothing in between. How did this come about? Chadwick found the answer; it was that the nuclei of the beryllium atoms contained, as well as protons, uncharged particles which were called neutrons.

What had happened was that the alpha-particles which bombarded the beryllium atoms had displaced some of these neutrons, knocking them out of the beryllium nuclei. These neutrons shot out towards the paraffin wax but they could not be detected because

53

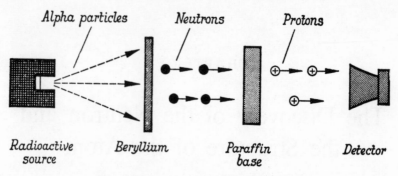

FIG. 59. Diagram of Chadwick's experiment

they had no charge. On hitting the wax they knocked protons out of the hydrogen in the wax and these protons, being charged particles, could be detected.

A new particle inside the nucleus had been discovered. The nucleus was now known to consist of protons and neutrons. Protons and neutrons were found to have very nearly the same weight; they differed in that the proton was positively charged and the neutron uncharged. These two particles, the proton and the neutron, together with the circling electron, made up the atom. They made up all the different atoms which exist—your table, your body, everything.

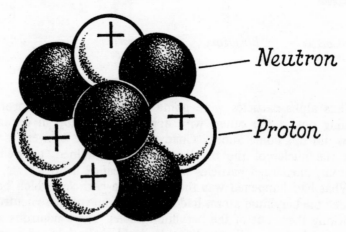

FIG. 60. Nucleus of an atom

Mass Number

Mass Number = number of protons + number of neutrons. The number of protons plus the number of neutrons in an atom of an element is called the Mass Number. Hydrogen, the lightest element, is the only atom with no neutron in its nucleus. The nucleus consists of one proton—Mass Number 1. The next heaviest atom, helium, has two protons plus two neutrons—Mass Number 4. Next, lithium, has three protons and four neutrons—Mass Number 7, and so on. In all atoms the number of electrons will equal the number of protons so that the charge balances.

The Mass Number is a whole number and approximately equal to the weight of the atom. The Atomic Weight of an element is not, however, exactly a whole number for reasons which will be considered later.

Atomic Number

Atomic Number = number of protons = number of electrons. Another term which is used in connection with the atom is the Atomic Number. The Atomic Number is the number of protons in the nucleus and therefore the number of electrons. Every element has a definite Atomic Number, a definite number of protons in its nucleus. Thus the Atomic Numbers of hydrogen, helium and lithium are respectively 1, 2 and 3. This is the order in which elements are arranged in the Periodic Table; it is the Atomic Number of an element which determines its chemical properties.

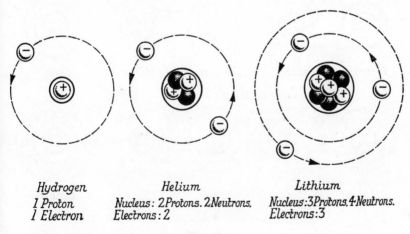

Hydrogen	Helium	Lithium
1 Proton	Nucleus: 2 Protons. 2 Neutrons.	Nucleus: 3 Protons. 4 Neutrons.
1 Electron	Electrons: 2	Electrons: 3

Fig. 61

55

With the discovery of the neutron, we had a complete picture of the nucleus. But to get a complete picture of the atom as a whole we need to know how the electrons are placed with respect to the nucleus. The structure of an atom can be compared with the structure of our solar system but there is an important difference. In our solar system each orbit or path contains only one planet, whereas in an atom a single orbit may contain as many as thirty-two electrons. It was Bohr, the Danish scientist, who first worked out the position of these orbits and the number of electrons which they contained. He found that the electrons are confined to definite orbits which we can number 1, 2, 3, etc., according to their distance from the nucleus, number 1 being the orbit nearest the nucleus. Orbit number 1 can contain a maximum of 2 electrons, orbit number 2 a maximum of 8 electrons, orbit number 3 a maximum of 18 electrons. Going from element to element in the Periodic Table, starting with hydrogen, electrons are added one after another, filling each orbit in turn. Thus hydrogen has 1 electron in orbit 1. Helium has two electrons in orbit 1—this orbit is now full. Lithium has 2 electrons in orbit 1 and 1 electron in orbit 2. Beryllium with 4 electrons has 2 in orbit 1 and 2 in orbit 2, and so on, until neon is reached when orbit 2 is full. The next sodium with 11 electrons has 2 in orbit 1, 8 in orbit 2 and 1 in orbit 3 and so on.

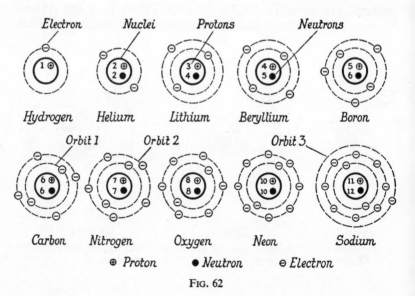

Fig. 62

FIG. 63. Sir John Cockcroft, who split the atom with protons

FIG. 64. Sir James Chadwick, who in 1932 at the Cavendish Laboratory discovered the neutron

FIG. 65. Dr. Enrico Fermi, who in 1942 made the first atomic pile

FIG. 66. O. Hahn, first to split the uranium nucleus in 1938

BRITAIN'S ATOMIC POWER STATIONS

Fig. 67. Chapel Cross in Scotland (140 megawatts)

Fig. 68. Artists' impression of Hunterston in Scotland—320 megawatts

Fig. 69. Artist's impression of Berkeley in Gloucestershire (275 megawatts)

If the orbits of an atom are completely filled, the structure is stable and the elements are inert. Thus the most inactive elements are the rare gases where the orbits are filled: helium (atomic number 2), neon (10), argon (18), krypton (36), and xenon (54). Atoms having one electron more than these, lithium (3), sodium (11), potassium (14), rubidium (37) and caesium (55), are all very active chemically and have similar properties. The same is true of atoms having one electron less: fluorine (9), chlorine (17), bromine (35), iodine (53).

If the number of protons in a nucleus is altered, as in the atom splitting experiments of Rutherford and Cockcroft, it becomes a different element with different chemical properties. Thus in the Cockcroft experiment a nucleus with three protons, lithium, is changed into a nucleus with two protons, helium. But in chemical reactions, such as combustion, the atoms merely re-group themselves by a re-arrangement of their electrons, and the nucleus is completely unaffected. Thus when two atoms of oxygen combine

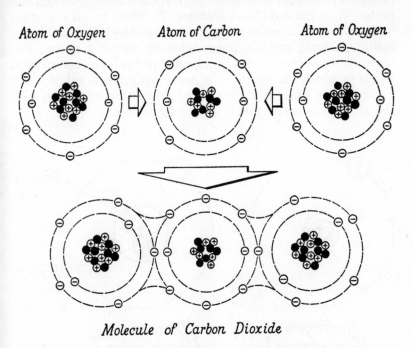

Molecule of Carbon Dioxide

FIG. 70. Two atoms of oxygen combine chemically with one of carbon to form a molecule of carbon dioxide

chemically with one atom of carbon to form a molecule of carbon dioxide, the electrons are re-arranged and shared but the nuclei remain unchanged.

Isotopes

As the chemical properties of an atom depend only on the number of protons in the nucleus, the number of neutrons can vary without affecting the chemical properties of the atom. As far back as 1912 Thomson had discovered that the gas neon consisted of two kinds of atoms. These had identical chemical properties but one had an atomic weight of 20 while that of the other was 22. The only difference between these two atoms was that one contained two more neutrons than the other. Atoms of different weight belonging to the same element, that is, with the same Atomic Number, are called isotopes.

Another example is hydrogen. The nucleus of hydrogen normally consists of one proton (Mass Number: 1). But one in every six thousand hydrogen atoms is different. It has a neutron as well as a proton in its nucleus (Mass Number: 2). These atoms are called heavy hydrogen atoms or deuterium. Normal hydrogen and heavy hydrogen atoms are indistinguishable by chemical means. For example, water is a chemical compound of hydrogen and oxygen. Water in which the hydrogen is heavy hydrogen is called heavy water. Heavy water is a clear liquid identical in every way with ordinary water except that it weighs 11 per cent more.

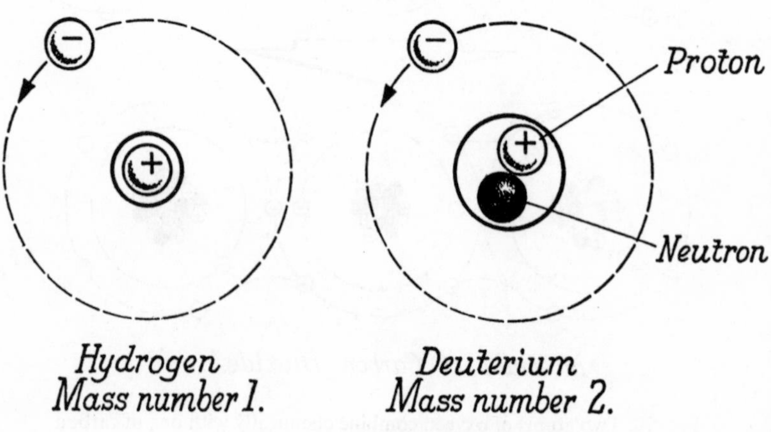

Hydrogen
Mass number 1.

Deuterium
Mass number 2.

FIG. 71. Isotopes of hydrogen

Experiments which began in 1919 showed that many isotopes existed. There are more than 250 isotopes of the 92 elements; tin has no fewer than 10 isotopes. Elements are in fact normally made up of isotopes, with different numbers of neutrons and therefore different weights. The Atomic Weight of an element is therefore an average weight and, unlike the Mass Number, rarely a whole number.

Chadwick's discovery of the neutron therefore constituted another important stage in understanding the structure of the atom. But it also proved to be important in another way for, as we shall see, it provided a new and powerful bullet for splitting the atom and made atomic energy a practical proposition.

CHAPTER 6

The Neutron in Action

PRIOR to the discovery of the neutron in 1932, two particles had been used to split the atom. From 1919, when Rutherford split the nitrogen atom, alpha particles were used, and in 1932 Drs. Cockcroft and Walton used protons. Both alpha particles and protons are positively-charged so are repelled by positively-charged nuclei. The charge on the nucleus acts as an electric barrier and most of the alpha particles or protons which are fired are deflected before reaching their target (Fig. 42). Alpha particles and protons could therefore only be used effectively if they travelled at a sufficiently high speed to penetrate the barrier. Moreover, alpha particles or protons could only be used successfully for splitting atoms of the lighter elements. Consider, for example, uranium, the heaviest element found in nature. The uranium nucleus contains 92 protons. A charged bullet, such as an alpha particle or a proton, would have to be extremely fast to overcome the strong repulsive force of these 92 protons packed into the nucleus. When the bullet got anywhere near the nucleus the repulsive force would be sufficient to deflect it or even hurl it back. A charged bullet has therefore very little chance of even touching the nucleus of such a heavy atom, let alone splitting it.

But the neutron is different. Having no charge, there is no force to stop it. Unaffected by the charge on the nucleus or electrons, it moves easily through atoms until it makes a direct hit on a nucleus. Neutrons are therefore much more effective bullets than charged particles for atom splitting. If we use neutrons as bullets we may expect that a fair proportion will break up nuclei instead of only one every million or so as with charged particles.

Shortly after its discovery the neutron was successfully used to split many atoms, including nitrogen, neon, fluorine and oxygen. The most important development was, however, the splitting of the uranium nucleus which was first fully investigated by the German scientists Hahn and Strassmann. Uranium is a very dense black metal, the heaviest element that occurs in nature. All uranium atoms contain 92 protons and 92 electrons. There are two main isotopes. The first is known as Uranium 238 because its nucleus contains 238 particles, 92 protons and 146 neutrons. The second, much more rare, has 92 protons and 143 neutrons and is therefore called Uranium 235.

Nuclear Fission

In the examples of atom splitting which we have considered so far, atomic bullets had done no more than chip a piece off the nucleus. But the Uranium 235 nucleus turned out to be unique. A bombarding neutron splits the Uranium 235 nucleus into two roughly equal halves; electrons collect round each half and two new atoms such as barium and krypton are formed. Gradually a picture was built up of what happened when the neutron struck the nucleus—a picture of the uranium nucleus stretching, forming a waist and finally breaking in two. This resembled the way that living cells divide, and biologists call it fission. The splitting of the uranium nucleus was therefore called nuclear or atomic "fission". The two new atoms produced, such as barium or krypton, are called "fission" products.

The fission of a Uranium 235 nucleus is accompanied by a powerful flash of gamma rays and a violent release of energy. This surplus energy drives the fission products apart at enormous speeds. They quickly lose their speed by colliding with surrounding atoms and their energy of movement is converted into heat just as the brakes on a car or a bicycle get hot when they are applied. In this way most of the energy is converted into heat and a considerable amount is released. A relatively large amount of mass is annihilated, and splitting one nucleus liberates 10 times more energy than any other nuclear transformation. The energy released by one nuclear fission is some sixty million times greater than when an atom of carbon in coal joins with oxygen to produce heat in our fires.

The amount of energy released from one fission would be of little use; about 31 million million fissions a second are needed to produce the heat of a one kilowatt electric fire. When however a Uranium 235 atom splits, two or three neutrons are released. Suppose for simplicity two neutrons are released per fission. Both of these would continue on their path until each hits another Uranium 235 nucleus. The splitting of these two nuclei will produce

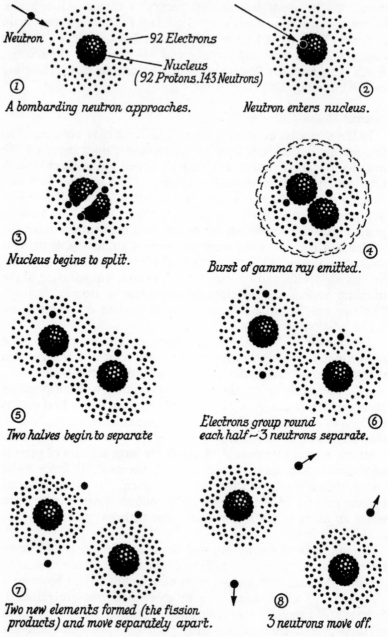

FIG. 72. Diagram showing progressive stages in the fission of a Uranium 235 atom

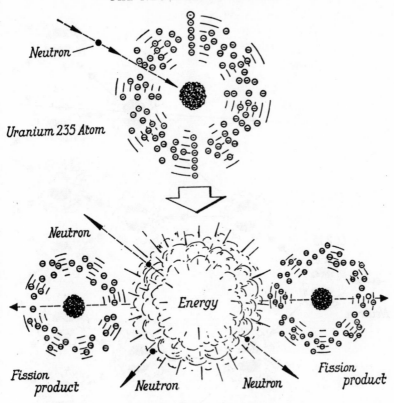

FIG. 73. Fission of Uranium 235

four neutrons. These will in turn split four nuclei and produce eight neutrons and so on. Clearly in this way the number of neutrons and the number of fissions will grow extremely rapidly. This process, called a "chain reaction", is the key to the release of atomic energy on a larger scale (Fig. 74).

The stages in nuclear fission can therefore be summarized as follows: a bombarding neutron strikes a Uranium 235 nucleus; the nucleus splits roughly in half, violently releasing energy; the two halves form new atoms such as barium and krypton, and two or three neutrons are released, each capable of splitting another U 235 atom, of starting, in other words, a chain reaction.

Material which is capable of nuclear fission is said to be fissile. One fissile atom which occurs in nature is Uranium

65

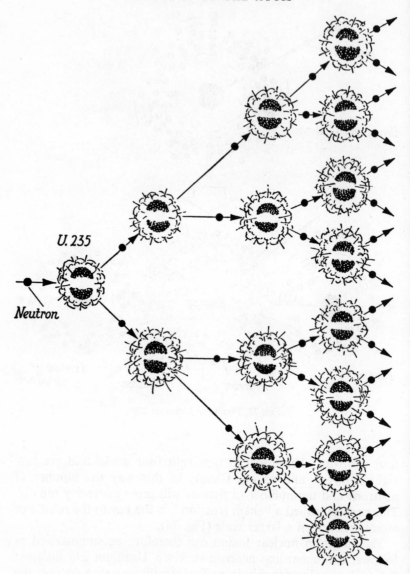

U. 235

Neutron

FIG. 74. A chain reaction

235. This is present in natural uranium but the amount is very small. In natural uranium only 4 atoms in 600 are of the fissile Uranium 235 variety; the rest are Uranium 238 atoms. A

FIG. 75. CALDER HALL, the first industrial-scale atomic power station in the world

FIG. 76. Control room at Calder Hall

FIG. 77. Uranium rods for the Calder Hall reactor

FIG. 78. Top of reactor, where uranium rods are inserted

stray neutron hitting natural uranium may cause a fission and two or three neutrons will be released. But these neutrons will stand little chance of hitting fissile atoms which are so few and far apart. So slender is this chance that a chain reaction in natural uranium is impossible.

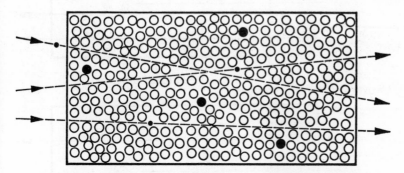

• *Neutrons.*   ● *Uranium 235 Nuclei.*   ○ *Uranium 238 Nuclei.*

FIG. 79. In natural uranium, Uranium 235 nuclei are so few and far between that they stand little chance of being hit by neutrons

The atomic pile or reactor

It would therefore appear impossible to use natural uranium as a source of atomic energy. This would have been so but for an important discovery by Fermi, an Italian scientist. This discovery concerned the behaviour of neutrons. The neutrons released during fission shot out at great speed; they travel at about 10,000 miles per second. Fermi found that neutrons could be slowed down by making them pass through certain substances. The process of slowing down neutrons is called moderation and the material in which this process takes place is called a moderator. Substances with nuclei much larger than neutrons are unsuitable as moderators; this is because a neutron, when it hits a large nuclei, will rebound with almost the same speed, and no slowing down is achieved. On collision with very light nuclei, however, more of the energy of the neutron is transferred to the nuclei at each collision and the neutron is gradually slowed down. Light elements such as carbon or beryllium therefore make good moderators and can slow neutrons down to speeds of about 15 miles per second.

Fermi found that the efficiency of these slow neutrons as bullets, far from being diminished, was increased a thousand-fold. It was

69

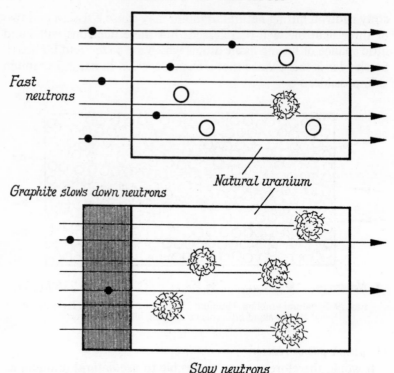

Fast neutrons

Graphite slows down neutrons

Natural uranium

Slow neutrons

FIG. 80. Slow neutrons are more effective than fast neutrons in splitting
Uranium 235 nuclei

rather like a golfer trying to sink a putt; the golf ball is the neutron
and the hole is the fissile nucleus. If the ball is hit hard and travels
fast, it is unlikely to go into the hole even if it travels in the right
direction. A slow ball, on the other hand, is much more likely to
drop into the hole. In a similar way, slow neutrons were readily
captured by Uranium 235 nuclei and were much more effective in
producing fission than were fast neutrons. Could a chain reaction
be sustained in natural uranium if slow neutrons were used?

Fermi set out to find the answer. In 1938 he and his family
emigrated to the United States, leaving Italy to escape life under
Fascism. In a disused squash court at the University of Chicago he
built up a large pile of carbon in the form of graphite to act as the
moderator. In this were inserted rods of natural uranium—several
tons were needed to give every neutron the opportunity of striking

a Uranium 235 nucleus. On December 2nd 1942, the work was completed; a chain reaction started, the first atomic pile, or reactor, as it is now more often called, had begun to operate. Although the amount of power produced was small — only about 200 watts—this was an historic event, the opening of the atomic age.

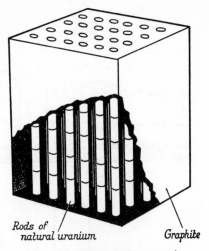

Rods of natural uranium

Graphite

FIG. 81. Diagram of an atomic reactor

The Atomic Bomb

The atomic reactor showed that if a lot of natural uranium were used and if graphite were used to moderate or slow down the neutrons, a chain reaction could be sustained. We will see later that in an atomic reactor this reaction can be controlled so that each fission gives rise to just one further fission and thus to a continuous production of energy. But supposing, instead of natural uranium, in which only 4 out of 600 atoms are fissile, pure uranium 235 were available. In uranium 235 every atom would be fissile and a chain reaction could be obtained without using a moderator. The amount of uranium 235 used would however be important and the deciding factor. Suppose in a small piece of Uranium 235 a stray neutron caused a fission. Two or three fast neutrons would shoot out but before they had gone far they would reach the surface and escape into the air. They might well reach the surface without hitting a nucleus; one or two fissions might occur but the action would soon peter out. With a larger piece of Uranium 235, a higher proportion of neutrons would have the chance of hitting nuclei before escaping. The size could be increased until the number of neutrons causing fission was just sufficient to maintain a chain reaction, each fission giving rise to one further fission. This is called the critical size. Supposing two pieces of Uranium 235, each slightly less than the critical size, were brought together. The amount of Uranium 235 would now be super-critical. With this amount of fissile material many more neutrons would bring about fission—a relatively small number would reach the surface and

71

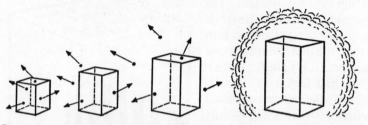

Block of pure uranium 235. Many neutrons escape without causing fission, no chain reaction.   *When critical size is reached – chain reaction – each fission gives rise to one further fission.*

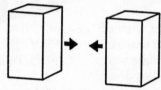

Two blocks of pure uranium 235 each just under critical size are moved together.

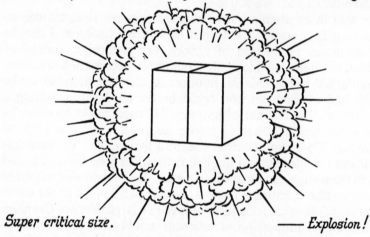

Super critical size.   *—— Explosion!*

FIG. 82. *How an atomic bomb works*

escape. A single neutron would be sufficient to initiate a chain reaction. When this neutron struck a nucleus and caused fission, two neutrons would be released. Both of these would continue on their path and split two further nuclei, producing four neutrons. In the next "generation" there would be eight neutrons, and after

72

twenty generations about a million neutrons would have been produced. In pure Uranium 235 these neutrons would only have to travel a short distance before encountering a nucleus. A staggering amount of energy would therefore be released in an extremely short time; it would in fact produce an explosion, an atomic bomb. Two pounds of Uranium 235 would produce an explosion equivalent to some twenty thousand tons of TNT. This is the very opposite of the controlled reaction of an atomic pile. The two applications of atomic energy are as different as the burning of coal and the detonation of TNT.

One of the primary problems in making an atomic bomb was therefore how to separate the vital Uranium 235 from Uranium 238 in natural uranium. This presented many difficulties for both Uranium 235 and Uranium 238 are isotopes of the same element. They therefore have identical chemical properties and cannot be separated by chemical methods. Eventually scientists and engineers working under the "Manhattan Project" devised satisfactory methods of producing the isotope Uranium 235 in a pure form, and the necessary large-scale plant was constructed. This resulted in the atomic bomb which destroyed Hiroshima in Japan on August 6th 1945, helping to bring World War II to an end.

CHAPTER 7

Power from the Atom

IN December 1942 the first atomic pile began to operate but much further research was needed to make atomic energy available on an industrial scale. It was fourteen years later when the first industrial-scale atomic power station in the world came into action. This was the Calder Hall power station in Cumberland, which began feeding electricity into the national grid on October 17th, 1956. The energy of the atom had been harnessed not for destruction but for man's service.

To appreciate the significance of this development, we need to understand something of the economic effects of an abundant and cheap source of fuel.

In the reign of Queen Elizabeth I (1558–1603) the population of Great Britain was some four millions, mostly employed in agriculture. Coal production was about 200,000 tons. Timber, the main source of fuel, was already scarce, and its price rose substantially during the reign. The advent of the steam engine, which enabled energy to be generated from fuel, brought in a new era. In 1800 production of coal was 10 million tons and the population was nine millions. By 1913 it had risen to 287 million tons, with exports of 94 million tons, and the population to 41 millions. Without large quantities of cheaply-mined coal, this industrial revolution and the rapid growth in population and wealth which took place in Great Britain during the late eighteenth and the nineteenth century would have been impossible.

Today industrial activity and the wealth of the country are more than ever dependent on the possession of adequate energy. A rising standard of living demands an increasing supply of energy for production in the factories, transport, heating, etc. To maintain this progress, it is estimated that the fuel consumption in Great Britain will by 1975 have reached the equivalent of 375 million tons of coal a year. A high proportion of this fuel will be required in the form of electricity; in 1955 about one-fifth of the coal mined in this country was used to generate electricity, and electricity consumption is increasing yearly at a rate equivalent to a doubling of output every ten years.

How can this increased demand for energy be met? Coal is our most important source and will continue to be for many years to come. Oil is increasingly being used but this has to be imported and in itself cannot fill the gap. Moreover, coal and oil are fossil fuels; when we burn these we liberate energy from the sun, stored for us by trees that grew and died millions of years ago. These reserves are being rapidly used up. Looking into the future, we can foresee a time, perhaps by the end of the century, when the world's resources of oil will begin to be exhausted, whilst our demand for energy will have grown enormously.

Clearly, therefore, there was a vital need for a new source of energy on which future industrial progress depended. The significance of Calder Hall is that it demonstrated that atomic energy could meet this need.

Calder Hall

A conventional power station is fired by coal or oil. The burning fuel in the furnace heats a large number of water-filled tubes in a boiler. The water in these tubes boils and turns into high pressure steam. This is fed to a turbine which drives an electric generator. The exhaust steam from the turbine is converted back to water in a condenser and returned to the boiler.

The manner in which an atomic power station works is essentially the same except that the heat is produced not by burning a fuel but by nuclear fission in an atomic reactor. This heat is transferred to the boiler by carbon dioxide; the carbon dioxide gas is blown through the reactor where it is heated and then to the boiler where it heats the water. The steam produced drives the turbines and generates electricity as in a conventional power station.

The Calder Hall power station took three years to design and three years to build. It consists of two nuclear reactors feeding four steam turbines. It uses natural uranium and the moderator is graphite. Each reactor consists of about 58,000 graphite blocks built in the form of a cylinder about 36 feet in diameter and 27 feet high. This mass of graphite forms the core of the reactor and weighs about 1,200 tons. Vertically through it run 1,696 parallel holes, or "channels" as they are usually called.

Rods of natural uranium, 1·15 in. in diameter, and a few feet long, are lowered into the channels from the charge face and stacked, one on the other, until each channel is filled with six rods standing end to end. About 130 tons of uranium rods are required; each rod is contained in a magnesium alloy case to prevent any dangerously radioactive fission products from escaping.

The reactor is regulated by control rods which through special channels can be raised or lowered into the graphite core. These control rods contain boron which strongly absorbs neutrons. The

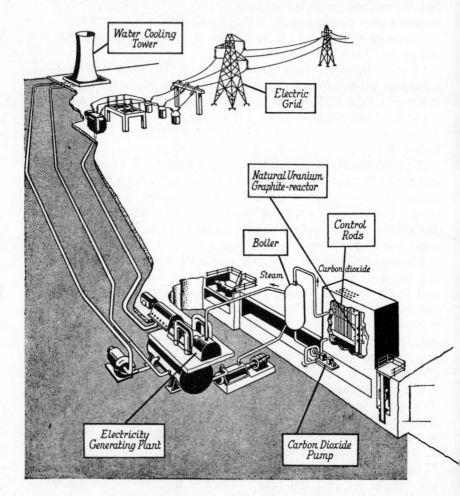

FIG. 83. Diagram of an atomic power station

FIG. 84. Explosion of an atomic bomb

FIG. 85. The *Nautilus*—American nuclear-powered submarine

FIG. 86. An atomic reactor (BEPO) at the Atomic Energy Research Establishment, Harwell, used to produce radio-isotopes

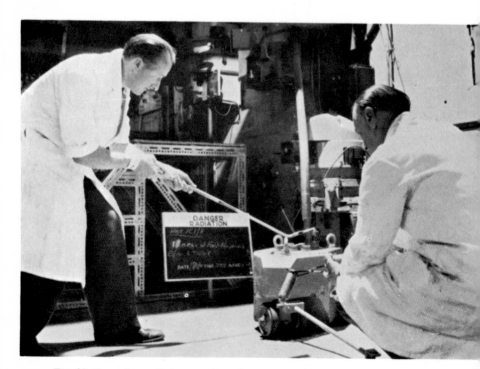

FIG. 87. Removing radio-isotopes from the reactor and placing them in a lead container

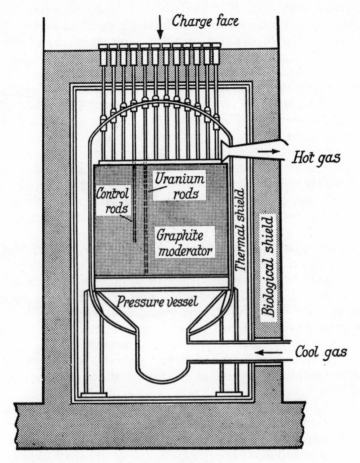

Fig. 88. The reactor

number of neutrons absorbed depends upon the length of the control rods projecting into the core. When they are lowered right into the core, a large number of neutrons is absorbed; this decreases as the control rods are withdrawn.

Suppose we begin with the control rods lowered right into the core. Fast neutrons released by fission in the uranium rods escape into the graphite moderator. The uranium rods are sufficiently wide apart for each neutron emitted in a fission to suffer several hundred collisions and become quite slow before it enters another uranium rod. In such a large core these slow neutrons are bound to strike other rods of natural uranium or be absorbed by the control rods. With the control rods fully lowered, so many will be absorbed that of the two or three neutrons produced during fission less than one will cause a further fission. A chain reaction will be impossible and the action will peter out. As the control rods are removed from the core, fewer will be absorbed and more will become available for fission. The stage will be reached when at each fission one of the released neutrons produces a further fission. A chain reaction will then have been established with a continuous production of energy. To maintain a constant rate of fission and to avoid any drift up or down, the position of the control rods is adjusted automatically. As a safety precaution, shut-off rods are also provided—if the number of fissions becomes excessive, these neutrons absorbing rods are automatically slammed in and shut down the reactor completely.

The heat generated by fission in the uranium rods is removed by carbon dioxide gas which is forced through the core between the rods and the channel walls. This type of plant is therefore called a gas-cooled, graphite-moderated nuclear reactor. In passing through, the carbon dioxide is heated and leaves the core at a temperature of 350° C. As the carbon dioxide is under pressure, the whole core must be surrounded by a steel vessel. This vessel is some 40 feet in diameter and 60 feet high and is made of 2 inch steel to withstand a pressure of about 7 atmospheres or 100 lb. per square inch.

During fission gamma rays are radiated and neutrons emitted. Both gamma rays and neutrons are dangerous to man as indeed are most forms of radioactivity and X-rays. Now radioactivity is not new. There had always been radioactivity everywhere. Some of it comes from cosmic rays—extremely penetrating rays which come from outer space. Some of it comes from radioactive substances on the earth itself. Radioactivity is in fact something like sunlight; we are exposed to it all our lives and our bodies accept a certain amount without ill effects. But radioactivity above a certain limit will make us ill and more will kill, producing a malignant blood disease called leukæmia. Stringent safety precautions are therefore taken to ensure that the amount of radioactivity which escapes from the reactor is well below the harmful level. To provide this protection, the steel reactor vessel is surrounded first by a shield of steel 6 inches thick and, outside this, by concrete, about 7 feet thick. This protection is called the biological shield.

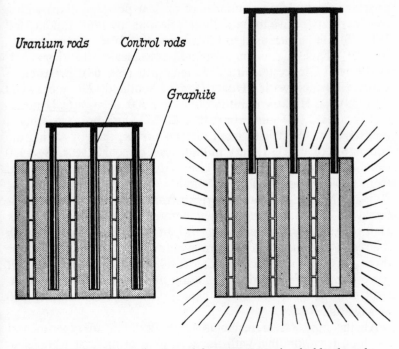

FIG. 89. Action of control rods: on left, neutrons are absorbed by the rods and there is no chain reaction. On right, the rods are withdrawn and a chain reaction is produced

The hot carbon dioxide leaves the reactor and is blown over water-filled tubes in a boiler, usually called a heat-exchanger. Here the carbon dioxide gives up its heat to generate steam; the steam drives the turbines coupled to electric generators exactly as in a conventional coal-fuel power station. Having passed through the heat-exchanger and lost its heat, the carbon dioxide is returned to the reactor again for reheating.

The output from Calder Hall is about 80,000 kilowatts. A single charge of uranium will last for some years until the nuclear reactor slows down and the uranium has to be changed. One ton of uranium split up by fission in the reactor will release as much heat as we get from burning three million tons of coal.

Further Developments

The experience of Calder Hall resulted in the preparation of a ten-year programme for nuclear power in Great Britain. This

81

provided for building a number of nuclear power stations with a total capacity of five to six millions kilowatts by 1965. Calder Hall (Fig. 75) will be increased to 140 megawatts. Other power stations include Chapel Cross in Scotland, 140 megawatts (Fig. 67); Berkeley in Gloucestershire, 275 megawatts (Fig. 68); Bradwell in Essex, 300 megawatts; Hunterston in Scotland, 320 megawatts (Fig. 69) and Hinkley Point in Somerset, 500 megawatts. (1 megawatt equals 1,000 kilowatts). Britain will then be generating a quarter of its electricity from nuclear power, thereby saving the equivalent of nearly twenty million tons of coal a year. By 1970 over 40 per cent of Britain's electricity supply will be provided from nuclear energy and it is estimated that the cost will then be 30 per cent cheaper than electricity from coal. The first stage is based on gas-cooled, graphite-moderated reactors of the Calder Hall type. Many improvements will, however, be embodied, with the result that the electrical power output for each station will be three or four times that of Calder Hall and the cost per unit correspondingly reduced. The station at Hinkley Point in Somerset, for example, will have a capacity of 500,000 kilowatts (500 megawatts).

All the time, research, including the building of experimental reactors, is continuing, with the aims first, of increasing the electrical output without a proportionate increase in the cost of the station, and secondly, of increasing the amount of heat extracted from each ton of uranium. The Calder Hall type of reactor uses natural uranium in which the uranium 235 (one atom in 140) undergoes fission while the bulk, uranium 238, is non-fissile. When, however, uranium 238 captures a neutron it turns into an isotope of a new element called plutonium which is not found in nature. This isotope, plutonium 239, is fissile just like uranium 235; a nucleus such as uranium 238, which is not itself fissile but becomes fissile when bombarded by neutrons, is said to be fertile. The neutrons captured by uranium 238 are therefore a good investment because they build up new fissile fuel, plutonium 239. In the Calder Hall reactor the new fuel is built up at about the same rate as the old fuel, uranium 235, gets used up. This does not mean that the uranium rods can be left in the reactor until all the uranium is used up. Before this occurs, fission products, some of which are strong neutron absorbers, will have poisoned the chain reaction; hence each rod periodically needs to be taken out and chemically purified.

In the Calder Hall reactor only just enough plutonium 239 is formed to replace the uranium 235 used up. A reactor, called a "breeder", can, however, be designed which will produce a considerable excess of plutonium. One of the main difficulties in producing pure fissile material from natural uranium is that of separating uranium 235 and uranium 238 because they are chemically identical—they are isotopes of the same element. Plutonium, being a different element with different chemical properties, can much more easily be separated from uranium. A breeder reactor, such as the Dounreay reactor, therefore provides a method of producing pure fissile material, plutonium 239, from natural uranium. This can be used for atomic bombs but it can also be used to enrich natural uranium for use as fuel in nuclear reactors. The enriched fuel has a higher proportion of fissile nuclei than natural uranium. A chain reaction can therefore be produced with a reduced amount of moderator, or, in fast reactors, with no moderator at all. Reactors can therefore be made smaller and more economic. Moreover, the abundant metal thorium is also fertile. Thus, although the starting material of nuclear power is the rare isotope uranium 235, the potential supplies of fuel which can now be used are enormously greater than this and comprise the whole of uranium and thorium. The known world resources of fuel are therefore sufficient to last for a very long time.

Different moderators are being used, such as heavy water, water, and beryllium instead of graphite. Instead of carbon dioxide various other substances are being used to transfer heat. These are called coolants and molten sodium, sodium-potassium alloy and water under pressure are being tried. In one type of reactor water is used both as a coolant and a moderator. There are therefore many kinds of future developments, but before changes are introduced, it would have to be proved in practice that they result in the production of cheap electricity.

What other applications of nuclear power shall we see? Will locomotives, motor cars, ships and aeroplanes be driven by mobile reactors? During fission, dangerous radiations are emitted and the reactor has therefore to be screened with massive walls of material such as concrete, steel or lead. One limiting factor in the use of atomic energy is therefore the weight of the nuclear reactor. Another difficulty is the danger arising from accidents which might involve damage to the shielding round the reactor. If this occurred, harmful radiation would escape, affecting people as well as crops and animals over a large area. It is unlikely therefore that nuclear power will be applied to land or air transport for commercial purposes. Suggestions have, however, been considered for large aircraft of about 200 tons. This would use only a minute quantity of fuel and fly continually over sea, say the Atlantic, towing conventional aircraft backwards and forwards. But there is much more promise for marine propulsion, for in a ship weight is not of primary importance. The driving-power required for a large ship would be about the same as that of a small power station of about 15,000 kilowatts output.

The feasibility of marine propulsion has been demonstrated by the U.S. submarine "Nautilus" which derives its power from a pressurised water reactor. This has travelled many thousands of miles and has a remarkable performance; it can sail for months, or years, without refuelling. Because of its nuclear power unit, it can remain submerged for long periods. In 1958 it completed a passage beneath the North Pole. It was submerged for 63 hours and travelled 1,830 miles under ice from Point Barrow in Northern Alaska to the Atlantic between Greenland and Spitzbergen. Other naval submarines and an icebreaker, "Lenin", built in U.S.S.R. are in operation but for merchant ships the economic factor is of major importance. To date, a nuclear marine power plant is not as economical as a conventional one. Research on specially designed reactors continues, and the most promising field is for large ships which spend most of their time at sea. The first nuclear-powered merchant ships are therefore likely to be oil-tankers or ore-carriers.

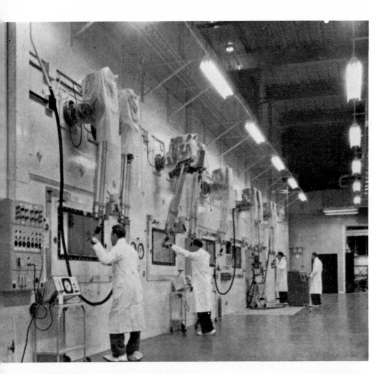

FIG. 90. Scientists operating mechanical hands. They are protected from radiation by thick concrete walls

FIG. 91 They can see through a window. The window, like an aquarium, consists of a solution of zinc bromide in water five feet thick; this gives the same protection as the concrete walls

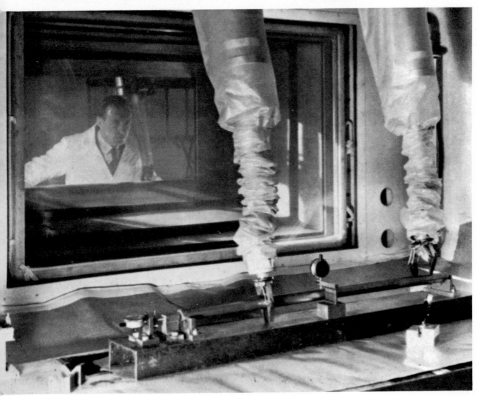

FIG. 92. A strong gamma source is used to "X-ray" a joint in a cylinder

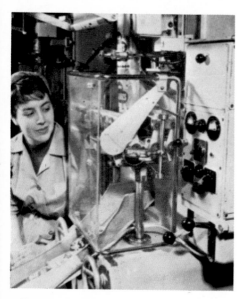

FIG. 93. Checking the contents of packets of biscuits; those incorrectly filled are rejected

FIG. 94. Radio-isotopes used to eliminate static electricity in a mill

CHAPTER 8

Radio-Isotopes

WE have seen how Becquerel first discovered radio-activity, and how his research was continued by the Curies. Then Rutherford discovered that radioactivity was caused by unstable atoms which exploded, emitting alpha particles, beta particles and gamma rays. The radioactive elements, such as uranium and radium, which they used in their experiments, all occurred in nature, in natural ores. Extraction and preparation was, however, laborious and expensive; radioactive elements such as radium were therefore both rare and very expensive.

In 1933 a method was discovered of producing radioactive elements artificially. They are now produced in large quantities and have many uses. They are made by bombarding stable elements with neutrons in an atomic reactor (Fig. 86). Take the element cobalt, for example. This is a metal closely related to iron and nickel and is not radioactive. Suppose a piece of cobalt is placed inside an atomic reactor and allowed to remain there for some time. When it is withdrawn it is strongly radioactive and this persists for a long time.

What has happened to the cobalt inside the reactor? An atom of the normal, naturally occurring cobalt has a nucleus consisting of 27 protons and 32 neutrons, giving an atomic weight of 59. We know that inside the atomic reactor there are millions of neutrons in rapid movement. These strike the cobalt and every so often one hits a nucleus and gets stuck. Eventually in this way a large number of cobalt atoms capture an extra neutron. These atoms will then each have 33 neutrons instead of the normal 32. These newly-created atoms are still cobalt because the number of protons has not changed. They are atoms of an artificial isotope of cobalt with the atomic weight of 60. Such atoms are not found in nature; they can only be made artificially.

Cobalt 59 and Cobalt 60, being isotopes, have identical chemical properties. The extra neutron, however, makes the nucleus of cobalt

60 unstable, like the nuclei of the natural radioactive elements such as radium and uranium; atoms of cobalt 60 change back to cobalt 59, and as each atom changes, a burst of gamma rays is emitted. Cobalt 60 has a half-life of 5 years 3 months. After this time half its atoms have changed to cobalt 59 and the radioactivity of the whole piece of cobalt is half of its original strength.

Many elements behave in this way. Lithium, for example, has 3 protons in the nucleus. There are two naturally-occurring isotopes —lithium 7 (4 neutrons), and lithium 6 (3 neutrons) which is much rarer. When lithium is placed in an atomic reactor, a third isotope is produced. This is lithium 8 with 5 neutrons in the nucleus. Lithium 8 is chemically identical with the other isotopes of lithium but its artificial atoms are unstable and emit radiation. With lithium 8 the radiation dies almost at once—it has a very short half-life.

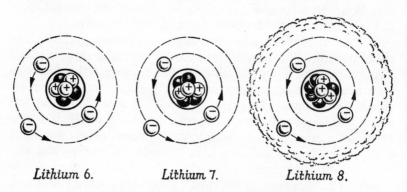

Lithium 6.   *Lithium 7.*   *Lithium 8.*

FIG. 95. Lithium 6 and Lithium 7 are natural isotopes;
Lithium 8 is a radioactive isotope

Isotopes which emit radiation are called radioactive isotopes or more commonly radio-isotopes. Scientists have now made more than 700 different radio-isotopes. Some of them emit strong radiations even more powerful than radium, and others are only feebly radioactive. The radiation may consist of alpha particles, beta particles and gamma rays; some may emit all, others mainly beta particles or only gamma rays. In all cases the radiation arises from unstable atoms changing into other atoms. The activity of a radio-isotope decays as the number of unstable atoms becomes less. Just as with naturally occurring radioactive elements such as radium and uranium, the rate of decay occurs in a regular manner and is unaffected by temperature, pressure or other conditions. Each radio-isotope has a characteristic half-life: that is, the time taken for half the unstable atoms originally present to change. This half-life may be anything from a fraction of a second to millions of years, depending on the radio-isotope.

Radio-isotopes have now many hundreds of uses in medicine, industry, agriculture and research. They can be used in two ways. Firstly: being radioactive they give off particles in rays which can be detected by sensitive instruments. In other words, the atoms of radio-isotopes are miniature wireless transmitters sending out signals which can be picked up by suitable receivers. Thus the presence of a radio-isotope can easily be detected, even in very small quantities, and its path traced. Thus radioactive sodium can be introduced into the body and used to trace the circulation of the blood. Similarly a radio-isotope introduced into the water of an underground water pipe enables the pipe to be traced from the surface and a leak quickly and easily detected. With radioactivity it is possible to label a single grain of sand and find it again or follow it for a long period without difficulty. Radio-isotopes used in this way are called tracers. Secondly, the radiations themselves can be used to replace X-ray equipment, to measure thickness of material, to kill bacteria and for many other purposes.

To provide for such a wide range of uses, many different radio-isotopes are required. For some purposes a weak radiation is required, sometimes with a short half-life so that the radiation ceases after a brief period. For other purposes a permanent source of intense gamma rays is required. Different radio-isotopes need therefore to be handled and packed in different ways according to the type of radiation emitted. This is carried out at the Radio-Chemical Centre, Amersham, where the radio-isotopes are prepared in a convenient form for use in industry. For some purposes the radioactive carbon 14 is required. This had a very long half-life, so the radiation is steady over long periods. Carbon 14 emits beta particles; these are electrons and are absorbed by a few inches of air or a thin sheet of metal. Carbon 14 can therefore be handled quite safely from behind a perspex window a few centimetres thick. A "glove box" is used consisting of a perspex box with a pair of gloves built in. The operator can by putting his hands in the gloves carry out the necessary manipulation on the carbon 14 and pack it in a relatively thin metal box.

Radio-isotopes emitting the penetrating gamma rays must be handled with great care, and elaborate safety precautions must be taken. A thick lead wall is needed to protect the operator and he must carry out his manipulations with "mechanical hands". These radio-isotopes must be stored in massive lead containers so that no dangerous rays are emitted. Some radio-isotopes are so active that a concrete wall three feet thick is needed for protection. For these, elaborate handling equipment has been devised. These "mechanical hands" are worked by remote control; the operator is situated some distance away and watches the manipulation by television. With these methods the radio-isotopes are prepared so that they can be used easily and with complete safety on industrial and scientific work.

Measuring Radiation

The use of radio-isotopes involves detecting and measuring the radiation emitted. Various methods are used, depending on the type and amount of radiation and kind of information required. Becquerel, when he discovered radioactivity, used the photographic plate as a means of detection, and this is still used for many purposes today. It depends on the fact that radiation causes fogging of the photographic plate; the extent to which it is fogged is a measure of the amount of radiation present. A photographic plate can also be used to take an X-ray photograph using a radio-isotope instead of the normal X-ray equipment.

An instrument, the gold leaf electroscope, for measuring radiation has already been described (page 29). This depends on the fact that radiation causes gases atoms to ionise, i.e. to separate into positive ions and electrons. The air inside the instrument, called the ionisation chamber, therefore becomes a conductor. The charge on the gold leaf breaks away and the leaf falls. The rate at which it falls is a measure of the amount of ionisation and therefore of the radiation. This simple principle is used in modern instruments but measured, not by a gold leaf, but by electrical methods and the amount of radiation can be read directly from a meter. This ionisation chamber method is used particularly for measuring relatively high intensities of radiation.

Another instrument which is used is the Geiger counter, which can detect individual radiations. The Geiger counter consists of two electrodes across which a voltage is applied. The tube contains air or some other gas at low pressure. If charged particles, X-rays

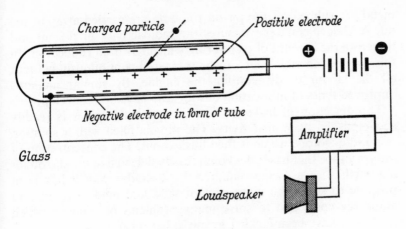

FIG. 96. Diagram of Geiger counter

or gamma rays enter the tube, the gas becomes ionised and the ions move rapidly towards the electrodes. The result is that a current flows in the electrical circuit to which the tube is connected. This will be repeated for each particle or burst of gamma rays entering the tube. The current is then passed through a valve amplifier and then to a loud speaker. A click will be heard for every particle or burst of gamma rays; the rapidity of the clicks indicates the strength of the radiation. Instead of connecting the amplifier to a loudspeaker, it can be connected to a counter which automatically counts the number of current impulses and thus measures the strength of the radiation from the radioactive source. This method of detecting radioactivity is extremely sensitive. It can be used to detect radio-isotopes even in amounts too small to be visible or to be traceable by ordinary chemical means. It is, for example, possible to detect about 10^{-16} of a gram of the radio-isotope phosphorus 32.

Radio-isotopes in Industry Tracers

(i) TRACERS. Radio-isotopes are used to determine the amount of wear in various moving parts of an engine. Suppose a new type of piston ring for a motor car engine is being developed. The ring is made radioactive by placing it in an atomic reactor or alternatively by including in it a small amount of suitable radio-isotopes. The engine is then assembled. When it is running, small amounts of

91

metal are rubbed off the piston ring and are carried away in the oil. A Geiger counter measures the radioactivity of the oil and therefore the amount of piston ring which has been rubbed off. In this way piston ring wear can be measured continuously without all the labour of dismantling the engine. By similar methods improved types of lubricating oils for cars have been developed.

The detection of leakage from oil and water pipes is readily accomplished by radioactivity. The pipe is filled with a solution of a radio-isotope which is then flushed out. The concentration of radio-isotope that has leaked out is easily detected in the surrounding earth with a Geiger counter. In a similar way it has been possible to study the movement of sand and mud in rivers and along the coast and to solve many problems of siltation which could not have been tackled by any other means.

There are hundreds of similar applications of radio-isotopes in industry. The small amounts of oil in nylon fibre can be determined in this way. The traces of one dye carried over into another dye bath can be measured. The quality of mixing can be controlled by adding radioactivity to one ingredient and then checking the finished product for radioactivity. All such applications depend on the fact that even a minute amount of radioactivity can readily be detected by sensitive apparatus such as a Geiger counter.

(ii) THICKNESS MEASUREMENT. The extent to which alpha and beta particles penetrate a substance depends on the nature of the substance itself and its thickness. If, for example, a piece of metal foil is placed between a radioactive source of beta particles and an ionisation chamber, the meter will show that a large number of beta particles have passed through the foil. If a thicker piece of foil of the same material is used, fewer will pass through and the meter reading will be smaller. If this is repeated, increasing the thickness of the metal each time, a stage will be reached when no beta particles will be able to penetrate, and the meter reading will then be zero. If we know the thickness of each piece of metal foil, we could find the corresponding meter reading. With this information we could measure the thickness of any piece of foil of the same material simply by taking the meter reading. We have therefore a method of measuring the thickness of the foil by using beta particles.

The great advantage of this method is that thickness can be measured without touching the material. It can therefore be

FIG. 97. A radioactive ring is fitted into the piston to measure engine wear

FIG. 98. Determination of the rate of flow of blood from wrist to wrist: a radio-isotope is injected into one wrist and a Geiger counter is placed over the other

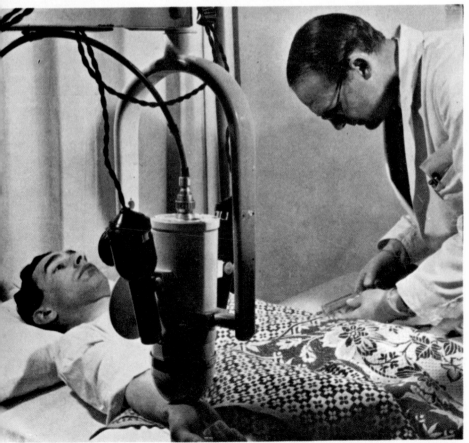

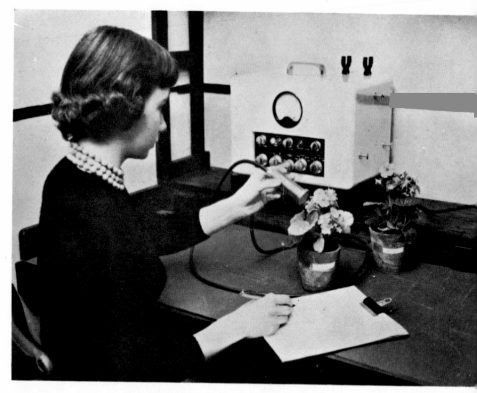

FIG. 99. Fertiliser research; here a plant has been fed with a radio-isotope solution. The amount in the flowers and leaves is being measured with a Geiger counter

FIG. 100. With a Geiger counter, leaks in a water main can be quickly detected

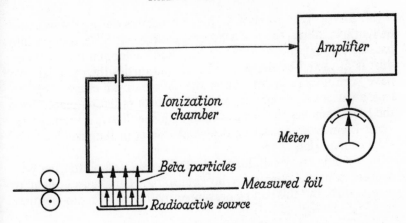

Fig. 101. Beta particle thickness gauge

applied to moving material and is used during the production of paper or thin metal sheet. It not only continuously measures the material during production but by electrical methods automatically corrects the machinery, so that the final product is of uniform thickness. It is therefore no longer necessary to stop the machinery to check thickness; measuring by radioactivity means that paper or metal sheet of accurate thickness can be produced continuously and automatically. Radio-isotopes emitting beta particles can be used in this way for thicknesses from thin tissue paper or ·0002 inch aluminium foil up to $\frac{3}{16}$ inch aluminium or $\frac{1}{16}$ inch steel. For greater thicknesses gamma ray sources are used, which extend their range up to 2 or 3 inches of steel.

A similar method is used to measure the contents of closed containers. To measure, for example, the liquid level in a closed tube, a radioactive source and a detector are mounted on opposite sides of the tube; the source is chosen so that its radiation penetrates the walls of an empty tube but not the contents. The detector can therefore measure the amount of liquid in the tube. In this way radio-isotopes can, for example, be used to check the contents of sealed tooth-paste tubes or packets of biscuits after automatic filling. By electrical methods those packages which are not correctly filled are automatically rejected. There are many applications to this type of equipment in use on conveyor belts in factories to detect and automatically reject empty or under-filled packages.

95

(iii) STATIC ELIMINATION. In many processes during the weaving of synthetic fibres, the fibres become charged with electricity while passing through the loom. At night, when the loom is not working, dust is attracted by the static charge and dirties the material. We have seen how radiation causes the charge on an electroscope to leak away. In a similar way a source of beta radiation placed near the loom removes the electric charge on the fibres; it thereby prevents them from collecting dust and results in the production of cleaner material.

In a similar way celluloid and other sheets of plastic material acquire a static charge during polishing. This causes them to attract dust, but this can be prevented by the use of radio-isotopes.

(iv) GAMMA RAYS. X-rays can be used to detect flaws in metal welds and castings. For example, when the plates of a ship are welded, the weld is inspected by X-rays to ensure a satisfactory joint. This process has been in use for some time and is invaluable in detecting flaws inside the metal which are not visible on the surface. But to produce X-rays which will penetrate thick steel, a 2-million-volt machine is required.

The same result can be obtained at much less expense by using gamma rays from suitable radio-isotope. Cobalt 60 is generally used for this purpose; it produces gamma rays roughly equivalent in penetrating power to a 2-million-volt X-ray machine. When using radio-isotopes which emit such penetrating and dangerous radiation, safety precautions are essential; the radio-isotopes are generally mounted in aluminium holders which, when not in use, are stored in heavy lead containers.

In practice, a photographic film (usually in a holder to exclude light) is place behind the metal to be examined. The radio-isotope is mounted at a distance on the other side. The gamma rays penetrate the metal and expose the plate. A picture of the inside of the metal is thus produced and any internal flaws are immediately revealed.

Radio-isotopes in Medicine

(i) TRACERS. Radio-isotopes are used in medicine and are of great value in diagnosing human disorders. Radioactive sodium, for example, can be prepared and from it sodium chloride. The properties of this sodium chloride will be identical with those of common salt except that it is mildly radioactive. It is therefore completely harmless and can be injected into the bloodstream. Its movement inside the body can be followed with a Geiger counter. In this way the blood flow from the arm to the heart can be timed exactly and this gives valuable information in diagnosing certain heart diseases.

Radioactive iodine is used in investigating disorders of the thyroid gland. This gland, which is situated in front of the neck, is important because it controls the development and functions of the body. A patient is given a liquid containing a small amount of radioactive iodine to drink and within a few hours the iodine is collected by the thyroid gland. A Geiger counter is used to measure the radiation in all directions. From this information the doctor can determine the size and position of the thyroid gland and the amount of iodine accumulated. This enables him to determine the state of health of the gland. An X-ray photograph of the neck would show nothing, but the radio-isotope of iodine may give the doctor sufficient information for an exact diagnosis and treatment. In a similar way, radioactive phosphorus is used to show the extent of brain tumours.

(ii) GAMMA RAYS. Penetrating X-rays, or gamma rays, from radium have for some time been used for treating cancer. Cancerous growths inside the body can often be controlled and eliminated by such treatment.

Radio-isotopes are cheaper than radium and can be selected with radiations best suited to any particular application. They are therefore increasingly being used for this purpose.

Sterilization is usually carried out by heating, but provided that a sufficiently large dose is given, gamma rays can kill most forms of living organisms including bacteria. They can therefore be used to sterilize penicillin and other antibiotics which must not be subjected to high temperatures. Because of the penetration of these rays this sterilization can be carried out after the antibiotics have been safely packed in sealed containers. Gamma rays can also be used to sterilize hypodermic needles and even hospital bedding, which it is important should be free from bacteria which can cause infection.

Radio-isotopes in Food and Agriculture

(i) TRACERS. Radio-isotopes are used as tracers to ensure efficiency of mixing. For example, in the manufacture of cattle-food, vitamin is added. A very small amount of vitamin has to be mixed with a large amount of cattle-food. The mixing must be thorough to ensure that each sample of cattle-food contains the same amount of vitamin. Before the use of radio-isotopes it was almost impossible for the manufacturer to guarantee that each sack of food contained the right amount of vitamin. Now a suitable radio-isotope is added to the vitamin and the amount in each sack can quickly and easily be found with a Geiger counter. The amount of radio-isotope used is small and one with a very short half-life is chosen; in this way the radio-activity has disappeared before the animal eats the food, and there can be no harmful effects.

By using fertilizers containing radio-isotopes it is possible to study the uptake mechanism of plants, their rate of growth and the importance of certain elements in the soil in producing healthy crops. Thus new and more effective fertilizers can be developed. Similar methods are used in developing insecticides.

(ii) GAMMA RAYS. We have seen that gamma rays kill bacteria and can therefore be used to sterilize instruments and drugs. Even a light dose of gamma rays greatly reduces the bacteria population and increases by four or five times the storage life of bacon, ham and sausage. A light dose of gamma rays will also inhibit the sprouting of potatoes, without in any way affecting their palatability.

Gamma rays are also used to kill or sterilize grain weevils and beetles in grain stores, where they do great damage and cause considerable losses.

These, then, are some of the many uses of radio-isotopes in industry, medicine, food and agriculture. Industry today is making wide use of radio-isotopes; one can hardly buy a finished article which has not seen a radio-isotope at some stage of production. New discoveries are continually being made and put to use. Radiation is also being employed widely in scientific research. It can, for example, be used to determine the age of archaeological specimens such as fossils, pottery or animal remains. This is because, as a result of cosmic ray bombardment from outer space, the carbon dioxide in the air contains small quantities of the radio-isotope carbon 14. This is taken in by plants during photosynthesis. All animal and vegetable carbon, therefore, contains carbon 14 derived either directly or indirectly from the carbon dioxide in the air. Upon the death of the animal or plant, the carbon 14 starts to decay. It has a half-life of 5,500 years. By measuring with a Geiger counter the carbon 14 content of an archaeological specimen, its age can be determined within about 100 years.

Radio-isotopes are therefore making a great contribution to the maintenance of health, the diagnosis and treatment of illness, food hygiene, the production of better and cheaper products and the general advance of scientific research and knowledge.

CHAPTER 9

Modern Research

THE last three chapters show that we have come a long way since J. J. Thomson in 1897 discovered the electron and thus proved that the atom could no longer be regarded as a solid indivisible sphere, the smallest particle of matter. The contributions of Rutherford, Chadwick and Bohr gave us the structure of the atom as a central nucleus of protons and neutrons with electrons circling round like planets round a sun. We have seen how one element can be transformed into another by splitting protons off the nucleus. We have seen that a new element can be made artificially—such is plutonium, an entirely man-made element, not found in nature. We have seen that radioactive substances can be produced artificially. We have seen that the energy released during fission can be harnessed to the service or destruction of man.

Many of these fundamental and brilliant discoveries were made with simple home-made apparatus. This was so with Thomson's discovery of the electron, Rutherford's discovery of the nucleus and Chadwick's discovery of the neutron. But to carry their work further much more complicated and elaborate equipment was required. We have seen how important discoveries were made by shooting atomic bullets at the nucleus of atoms, a technique invented by Rutherford. With this method Cockcroft and Walton in 1932 split the lithium atom with protons. They used about 300,000 volts to accelerate the protons but, even so, could only tackle a light element like lithium. To explore the atom more fully, much faster particles were needed. Enormous machines working on millions of volts have now been devised and built for this purpose. A modern version of the Cockcroft-Walton accelerator has been built at the Atomic Energy Research Establishment, Harwell. This machine, part of which is shown in Fig. 103, uses the equivalent of 0·5 million volts to produce very high-speed protons. These are required for the production of new isotopes, for atom splitting and

100

for investigations into the nature of the nucleus and the "atomic glue" which holds the protons and neutrons so tightly together in the nucleus.

Another machine for accelerating charged particles is the cyclotron. It was invented by Dr. E. O. Lawrence at the University of California in 1932. Since then, many cyclotrons have been built and have played an important part in atomic research. A cyclotron consists of two electrodes called "dees" because of their similarity in shape with a capital "D". Together they form a hollow flat pillbox cut along one diameter. (Fig. 102 [1]). They are placed in an evacuated container between the pole pieces of a very large electromagnet designed to produce a strong uniform magnetic field (Fig. 102 [2]). The dees are connected to a generator producing high frequency alternating current.

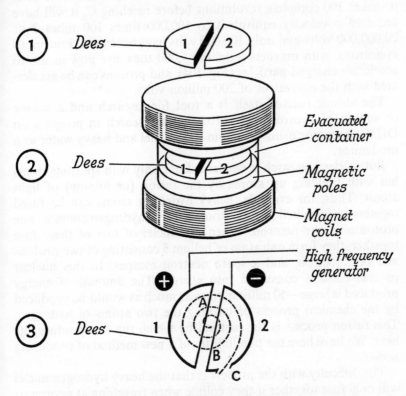

FIG. 102. The cyclotron: (1) the two dees. (2) The dees assembled between the pole pieces. (3) The path of a positively charged particle.

The source of charged particles, say protons, is at the centre. Suppose a proton arrives at A (Fig. 102 [3]). At that instant dee 2 is negatively charged with respect to dee 1, say 100,000 volts. The positively-charged proton will be attracted in the direction of dee 2 and greatly accelerated. Its path will however be bent by the magnetic field. The magnetic field is so strong in the cyclotron that the proton follows a circular path arriving at B. Now it is so arranged that by the time the proton has arrived at B the voltage of the dees (delivered to the dees by the high frequency generator) has changed; dee 1 is now negative and dee 2 is positive. So the proton gets accelerated again. Of course the frequency of changing the voltage on the dees has to be carefully adjusted so that the protons keep in step with it. If this adjustment is made, each proton will move on an expanding spiral, accelerating each time it crosses the gap between the dees, until it finally emerges at C. If it makes 100 complete revolutions before reaching C, it will have acquired a velocity equivalent to 100,000 times 100 times 2 or 20,000,000 volts and only 100,000 volts have been used. Enormous cyclotrons, with magnets weighing 3,000 tons, are now in use to accelerate charged particles (Fig. 104), and protons can be accelerated with the equivalent of 200 million volts.

The atomic reactor itself is a tool for research and a source of supply of neutrons. Fig. 105 shows research in progress on DIDO, a reactor using Uranium 235 as fuel and heavy water as a moderator.

But modern research is concerned not only with splitting atoms but with building up atoms by the fusion (or joining) of light atoms. Thus, for example, heavy hydrogen atoms can be fused together to form helium. An atom of heavy hydrogen contains one proton and one neutron. When the nuclei of two of these fuse together, they form one atom of helium 3 consisting of two protons and one neutron, and a spare neutron escapes. In this nuclear process mass is converted into energy. The amount of energy produced is large—50 million times as much as would be produced by the chemical process of burning the two atoms of hydrogen. This fusion process is the method by which the sun produces its heat. We have here the possibilities of a new method of producing power.

The difficulty with the process is that the heavy hydrogen nuclei will only fuse together if they collide when travelling at enormous speeds. One way of speeding up the heavy hydrogen atoms is to

FIG. 103. Modern Cockcroft-Walton particle accelerator

FIG. 104. A cyclotron

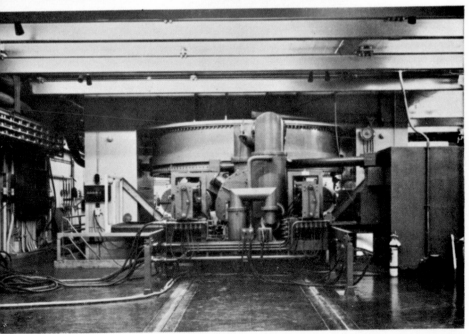

FIG. 105. Research in progre
on DIDO—a Uranium 23
reactor with heavy wate
moderator

FIG. 106. Zeta—first nuclear
fusion apparatus

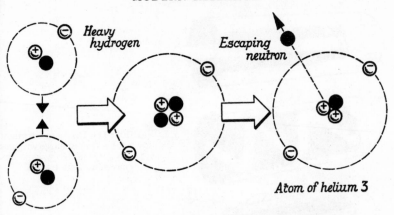

FIG. 107. Two atoms of heavy hydrogen fuse to form one atom
of helium

raise their temperature, but to get them going fast enough to produce fusion needs a temperature of several million degrees centigrade—far hotter than the surface of the sun. Such temperatures are reached in an atomic bomb and can produce fusion. This is how a hydrogen bomb works; the energy produced by fusion processes greatly adds to the explosive power of the bomb and the hydrogen bomb is many times more powerful than the atomic (fission) bomb alone.

But how could this fusion process be controlled and thus provide a practical source of power? This research is in its infancy but in 1958 British scientists and engineers at Harwell were able, with a new apparatus called ZETA, to heat up heavy hydrogen to temperatures of five million degrees. The vital part of ZETA is a discharge tube containing heavy hydrogen. A very large current is passed through the tube and the gas becomes extremely hot. As soon as the electric current begins to flow, the gas is automatically squeezed into a narrow column in the middle of the tube (Fig. 108 [1]). This happens because the current produces an intense magnetic field round the column of hot gas. This magnetic field squeezes the gas inwards so that it moves upwards away from the walls of the tube. Unfortunately as soon as the gas is squeezed it begins to wriggle and jump about inside the tube (Fig. 108 [2]). Unless this can be prevented the hot gas will touch the walls of the tube, lose its heat and melt the wall. In ZETA the gas is kept centrally in the tube and well away from the walls by winding coils

105

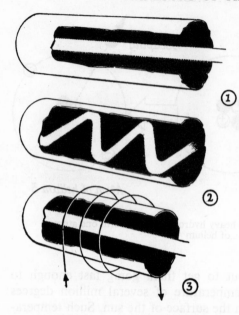

FIG. 108. (1) Discharge straight down tube; (2) discharge wriggles violently; (3) axial wriggle removed in Zeta by coil

of wire round the tube and passing electricity through the coils (Fig. 108 (3)). When this is done, the wriggle disappears.

In ZETA (Fig. 106) the discharge tube is a large container shaped like the inner tube of a motor-car tyre. It is called a torus. The torus is about twelve feet across and the tube of diameter of about three feet has thick aluminium walls. Heavy hydrogen is put into the tube, and electricity is passed through it from a transformer. Currents up to 200,000 amps. circulate in the closed torus. Round the tube of the torus there are large coils carrying electric current which keep the discharge away from the walls.

It is estimated that temperatures of 100 million degrees will have to be reached before a fusion reactor becomes a practical source of power. This may take many years but intensive research is being undertaken both in this country and elsewhere. What is the advantage of the fusion reactor which justifies all this research? The answer lies in the fuel, heavy hydrogen, which it uses. We get this from ordinary water—1 part in 45,000 of which is heavy hydrogen. It costs only a few shillings a gramme to separate heavy hydrogen from ordinary water and every gramme of heavy hydrogen fused into helium will produce as much power as 10 tons of coal. The heavy hydrogen atoms in a tumbler of ordinary water will produce as much energy as 20 gallons of petrol. So the fuel is not only cheap —its supply is inexhaustible. Moreover, a fusion reactor would have the advantage of not producing radioactivity or radioactive by-products; it might also be able to produce electricity directly without the use of conventional electric generators. So, although we have made great progress with atomic power stations throughout the country, we are really only at the beginning of our conquest of the atom, at the beginning of the atomic age.

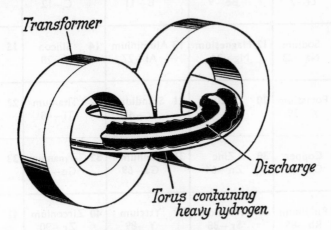

FIG. 109. The heart of Zeta: currents up to
200,000 amps circulate in a closed torus

PERIODIC TAB

1 Hydrogen H—1				
3 Lithium Li—7	**4** Beryllium Be—9	**5** Boron B—11	**6** Carbon C—12	**7** Nitrog N—1
11 Sodium Na—23	**12** Magnesium Mg—24	**13** Aluminium Al—27	**14** Silicon Si—28	**15** Phosphc P—3
19 Potassium K—39	**20** Calcium Ca—40	**21** Scandium Sc—45	**22** Titanium Ti—48	**23** Vanadiu V—5
29 Copper Cu—63	**30** Zinc Zn—64	**31** Gallium Ga—69	**32** Germanium Ge—74	**33** Arseni As—7
37 Rubidium Rb—85	**38** Strontium Sr—88	**39** Yttrium Y—89	**40** Zirconium Zr—90	**41** Niobiu Nb—9
47 Silver Ag—107	**48** Cadmium Cd—114	**49** Indium In—115	**50** Tin Sn—120	**51** Antimo Sb—12
55 Cæsium Cs—133	**56** Barium Ba—138	**57–71** Rare Earths	**72** Hafnium Hf—180	**73** Tantalu Ta—18
79 Gold Au—197	**80** Mercury Hg—202	**81** Thallium Tl—205	**82** Lead Pb—205	**83** Bismut Bi—20
87 Francium Fr—223	**88** Radium R—226	**89** Actinium Ac—227	**90** Thorium Th—232	**91** Protactin Pa—23

The top line in each box gives the name of the element an
chemical symbol of each element and the atomic weight of its

THE ELEMENTS

					2 Helium He—4
Oxygen O—16	9 Fluorine F—19				10 Neon Ne—20
Sulphur S—32	17 Chlorine Cl—35				18 Argon A—40
Chromium Cr—52	25 Manganese Mn—55	26 Iron Fe—56	27 Cobalt Co—59	28 Nickel Ni—58	
Selenium Se—80	35 Bromine Br—79				36 Krypton Kr—84
Molybdenum Mo—98	43 Technetium Tc—99	44 Ruthenium Ru—102	45 Rhodium Rh—103	46 Palladium Pd—106	
Tellurium Te—130	53 Iodine I—127				54 Xenon Xe—132
Tungsten W—184	75 Rhenium Re—187	76 Osmium Os—192	77 Iridium Ir—193	78 Platinum Pt—195	
Polonium Po—210	85 Astatine At—211				86 Radon Rn—222
Uranium U—238					

r of protons in its atomic nucleus. The second line gives the
on stable isotope.

APPENDIX 2

TERMS USED

ACCELERATOR: Apparatus used to accelerate charged particles (alpha particles, beta particles or electrons) to high velocities.

ALPHA PARTICLE: Helium nucleus, i.e. two neutrons and two protons; positively charged.

ANODE: Positive electrode.

ATOM: Smallest portion of an element which can take part in a chemical reaction.

ATOMIC NUMBER: The total number of electrons rotating round the nucleus of a neutral atom of an element or the number of protons in the nucleus.

ATOMIC WEIGHT: Weight of an atom of an element relative to the weight of the hydrogen atom (normally taken as relative to oxygen with atomic weight 16).

BETA PARTICLE: Fast moving electron emitted by radioactive substances.

CATHODE: Negative electrode.

CATHODE RAYS: Stream of electrons travelling away from the cathode in a discharge tube.

COMPOUND: Substance consisting of two or more elements chemically united in definite proportions by weight.

COSMIC RAYS: Very energetic radiation falling upon the earth from outer space and consisting of charged particles.

DEUTERIUM (HEAVY HYDROGEN): Isotope of hydrogen with nucleus consisting of one proton and one neutron.

ELECTRODE: Conductor by which electricity enters or leaves a discharge tube or other apparatus.

ELECTRO-MAGNETIC WAVES: Wide range of vibrations or waves travelling with velocity of 186,000 miles per second. In order of increasing wave-length they are: gamma rays, X-rays, ultra-violet, visible light, infra-red (heat) rays and wireless waves.

ELECTRON: Fundamental particle of matter of weight $\frac{1}{1840}$ that of the hydrogen atom and carrying a negative charge.

ELEMENT: Substance consisting entirely of atoms of the same atomic number.

FISSION (NUCLEAR): Process in which a heavy atom such as Uranium 235 splits in half with an enormous release of energy.

FLUORESCENCE: Property of absorbing radiations of one wave-length and emitting light of another wave-length.

110

GAMMA RAYS: Electro-magnetic waves of very short wave-lengths, shorter than those of X-rays.

HALF-LIFE: The time taken for the activity of a radioactive element to decay to one-half of its original value.

ION: Positive ions are atoms with fewer electrons than the normal neutral atom. Negative ions have more.

ISOTOPE: Atoms of the same element (i.e. having the same atomic number) but differing in atomic weight. This difference is due to a varying number of neutrons in the nucleus.

KILO: Prefix denoting a thousand.

MASS-ENERGY EQUATION: Mass and energy are mutually convertible under certain conditions. The equation connecting these two qualities is $E = mc^2$ where c is the velocity of light; E is the energy released when a mass of m is completely converted into energy.

MASS NUMBER: The total number of protons and neutrons in the nucleus.

MEGA-: prefix denoting a million.

MOLECULAR WEIGHT: The sum of the Atomic Weights in a molecule.

MOLECULE: Smallest portion of a substance capable of existing independently and retaining the properties of the original substance.

NEUTRON: Electrically uncharged particle present in the nucleus; approximately the same weight as the proton.

NUCLEUS (ATOMIC): Positively-charged body (consisting of positively-charged protons and neutrons) which forms the main mass of the atom.

RADIATION: The emission of any rays, waves or particles from a source.

RADIOACTIVITY: The spontaneous breakdown of unstable atomic nuclei, usually accompanied by the emission of charged particles and gamma rays.

SPECTRUM: The result obtained when electro-magnetic waves are separated according to wave-length: for example, when white light is separated into its constituents; these are (in order of decreasing wave-length) red, orange, yellow, green, blue, indigo, violet.

VACUUM: Space in which there are no molecules or atoms. A perfect vacuum is unobtainable and the term is generally taken to mean a space containing air or other gas at very low pressures.

X-RAYS: Electro-magnetic waves similar to light but of much shorter wave-length.

APPENDIX 3

Summary of Dates

1895 Röntgen discovered X-rays.
1896 Becquerel discovered radioactivity.
1897 J. J. Thomson discovered the electron.
1898 Pierre and Marie Curie isolated radium.
1903 Rutherford and Soddy put forward theory of radioactivity.
1905 Einstein's theory of relativity showing equivalence of mass and energy.
1910 Soddy suggested existence of isotopes.
1911 Rutherford discovered the nucleus.
1912 C. T. R. Wilson invented the cloud chamber.
1913 Bohr's theory of electron orbits.
1919 Rutherford split the atom—turned nitrogen into oxygen.
1925 Blackett, using cloud chamber, confirms Rutherford's transmutation of nitrogen into oxygen.
1932 Ccckcroft and Walton split lithium atom by proton bombardment.
1932 Chadwick discovered neutron.
1932 Lawrence built the first cyclotron.
1938 Hahn and Strassmann discovered nuclear fission.
1939 Frisch demonstrated nuclear fission.
1942 First atomic pile built by Fermi.
1945 Atomic bomb.
1956 Calder Hall, the first industrial-scale atomic power station.

Index